History and Evolution
of the
Fauna Conservation Laws of Botswana

Frontispiece: An example of the implementation of section 7 of Act 36 1886, which was repeated on several occasions in the "Bechuanaland News" in 1896, and formed the origin of Private Game Reserves.

History and Evolution
of the
Fauna Conservation Laws
of Botswana

Occasional Paper No. 3

Clive Spinage, DSc, PhD, BSc (Hons), FIBiol, was employed as a
consultant to the Department of Wildlife & National Parks from
1986 to 1991.

Published by the Botswana Society, Gaborone, 1991.

This publication has been sponsored
by
The World Conservation Union (I.U.C.N)

Cover illustration: "Lion in the Kalahari"
© Alec Campbell

First published 1991

ISBN 99912 60 09

Published by The Botswana Society
P.O. Box 71,
Gaborone,
Botswana

Printed by
MORIJA PRINTING WORKS
MORIJA – LESOTHO

FOREWORD

Botswana has been blessed with an abundance and variety of species of wild animals. Historical records show that even elephants, rhinos, giraffe, buffalo and zebra to mention but a few species, occurred in abundance in the Molopo-Nosop river valleys of the Kgalagadi Desert in the mid-nineteenth Century. Yet today they are not there – not necessarily on account of human interference only but also because of changing environmental factors as well.

However, Man has since been highly influential in the increasing adverse plight of Botswana's wildlife. A combination of increased hunting pressure, legal and illegal, for commercial gain; increasing human population and settlements with resultant constriction of land available to wildlife; general economic development activities of modern society including pastoral and arable land development and mineral prospecting and development have contributed to the present pressures on wildlife and its lands. For Batswana, their view is that these economic development activities should not be at the expense of wildlife which they have for a very long period of time lived with, admired, venerated, used, protected and held as their cultural heritage. Dr. Spinage has, in this review of the history of the fauna conservation laws of this country, amply demonstrated that for Batswana, conservation of the faunal resources in Botswana did not start because of today's world opinion. It started a long time ago, born out of need to protect a resource which was recognised as very valuable economically and culturally. Batswana, therefore, have all the right to be proud that their forefathers' judgement of a long time ago, has laid a foundation for today's wildlife conservation ideals now consolidated into the Wildlife Conservation Policy 1986. Our forefathers have thus left us a legacy, a valuable heritage. They have also left us a heavy responsibility – to continue to conserve this country's wildlife for enjoyment by future generations. If their approach has stood the test of time and enabled the present generation to enjoy this resource today, our present approach to wildlife conservation should likewise stand the test of time to enable future generations to enjoy this resource.

Dr. Spinage has made valuable contribution by consolidating the information in this publication of the "HISTORY AND EVOLUTION OF THE FAUNA CONSERVATION LAWS OF BOTSWANA".

K.T. Ngwamotsoko
DIRECTOR OF WILDLIFE AND NATIONAL PARKS
BOTSWANA

Gaborone May 1989

CONTENTS

Part I
History and Evolution of the Game Laws.

Introduction

With the possible exception of the numerous provincial game laws of the Republic of South Africa, Botswana has one of the most comprehensive game laws in Africa. There is much misconception as to its origin and, in recent years, some sectors of lay opinion have challenged the appropriateness of such law asserting that it is imposed from outside, *ab extra,* and thus has no pertinence to Botswana. This view seems, in part, to be compounded by the Courts, which, in recent years, have persistently awarded notoriously low penaltties for offences against the game laws. But resentment against game laws, where game is perceived as plentiful, is of universal nature. In France, consequent upon the 1790 Proclamation of the Revolution, the 17th century game laws,which forbade hunting except by the King and his appointees, were abrogated and hunting made the right of everyone *on his own possessions.* Yet in 1844 it was necessary to introduce a comprehensive legislation to stem the destruction, since the qualification of land ownership was ignored and it was feared that there would soon be no game left (Gillon and de Villepin, 1844). Game laws have invariably been imposed to ensure the survival of game[1], rather than as an irrational jealous denial to the individual, as is generally the rural dweller's interpretation. This often has the end result, as with any commodity, that as game becomes scarcer and more and more people want to partake of it, eventually the law is seen as being for the benefit of the richer sectors of the population who are able to pay for the privilege of hunting. But if there were no laws to exercise control, then the larger game animals would quickly disappear, for no value is placed upon something which has no ownership.

In Botswana, the exception to the rule prevailing in many other African countries, was that the statutory law introduced by the Protectorate Administration, applied principally to foreigners only, but reinforced customary law, the tribal chiefs introducing game laws at the request of the Administration. It was, however, inevitable, that such statutory laws would eventually come to be adopted for the country as a whole, since they were logical restraints imposed to meet changing circumstances. Nevertheless, it was not until 1979 that the statutory game laws became of universal application. But whereas the tendency for such laws in some post-independence African countries has been towards those of a less restrictive nature for the indigenous inhabitants (cf. Kenya's 'Wildlife (Conservation and Management) Act" 1976), an opposite trend can be seen in Botswana. Laws, previously liberal as far as the indigenous inhabitants were concerned, have, of necessity, shown a tendency towards tighter control. But there are usually compensatory differences, e.g. stricter control of firearms and ammunition in Kenya, and many protected areas[2].

The complex game law of Botswana has evolved partly in response to the dichotomous approach of one law for foreigners, and another for the indigenous inhabitants; submerging the ancient customary law of totems and taboos which was inadequate to meet the situation. Here, I examine how present law has evolved and attempted to trace its influences, whether they be customary attitudes, Roman, Dutch, English or other law.

Customary Law

According to Schapera (1938) Batswana traditionally could hunt wherever they pleased within the Tribal Territory, even over the fields and grazing lands of others, without making any payment[5], or giving any tribute. But this right, in general, only applied to small game, or meat for the pot; and even then there were qualifications concerning the age group of the hunters. Fur-bearing animals, however, were not usually hunted during the summer months when they were breeding, and Ngwato and Tawana, for example, recognised certain hunting preserves (see Part II). Hunting was therefore not without it's restrictions and it was subject to a number of strict conventions.

Totemic Law

The oldest form of customary law may be seen in totemic law. Traditionally the Tswana were divided into many groups, distinguished from one another by their totems which, in the majority of cases, was species of animals. Thus that of the Kwena and Ngwaketse royal families was the crocodile; of the Ngwato and Tawana the duiker; of the Kgatla the vervet monkey; of the Lete the buffalo; of the Tlokwa the antbear, of the Rolong the kudu, and of the Kalanga the baboon, zebra, elephant, buffalo and eland. One of the commonest obligations concerning a totem animal was that it could not be killed, or even touched. Thus was protection conferred on a range of animals.

Tribute Law

The other early restriction connected with hunting concerned the disposal of game that was killed. Among the Tswana, one opinion is that all game belonged to the Chief in trust for the Tribe and, as titular owner of the land, he was entitled to share in the proceeds of every hunting expedition (Schapera 1943). The role of the Chief in this respect is best understood by reference to Khama's interpretation of the position of the Chief (Khama 1971):

"The chief ... can, as the most senior member of the community, allocate to himself the most fertile parts of the land–the basis of this is that as head of the group, his comfort receives priority in the allocation of the use of all things which belong to the community because there is always a presumption that his first concern is for the community as a whole. He is the father of the community and under normal conditions as *pater familias* his administration of the communal property is unfettered even by custom unless it can be shown that his main concern is not the community but his personal welfare"[4].

Here, "all things which belong to the community" and "the communal property" we may interpret as including game, thus a hunter could not usually dispose at will of game that he had killed and might be obliged to give the whole, or specified portions, of it to the Chief, or to the elders, or to certain members of his own family.

The Chief received all animals killed in a collective hunt which he had organised *(letsholo)*[5]. Sometimes he divided the meat among those taking part, but usually suitable portions were dried and taken home for the people generally. The

Chief kept the skins or sold them. Individual hunters were obliged to give the Chief the brisket (*sehuba*) of large game, the skins of lions and leopards, one tusk of an elephant (that of the side on which it fell)[6], some feathers of an ostrich and the body of a bustard. As recently as 1935 the Kwena Chief insisted on his right to receive all skins of lion and leopard.

The leader of a regiment received all animals or game birds killed while the regiment was in the field. If there was enough meat he shared it. A junior regiment was obliged to hand over such game to a more senior regiment. No one at a cattle post, or in the veld, could eat game birds, small antelopes, hares or tortoises, without first offering them to elders. The offering was passed on until it reached the oldest member, unless anyone gave the junior permission to eat it. Among the Ngwato, the head and neck of large game, and the marrow of certain species like kudu and hartebeest, had to be handed to the elders. These regimental and seniority obligations were still customary law in 1940, the latter being strictly enforced; and they can be seen as limiting the individual's right to hunt animals.

The Kgalagadi, San, Bayei, Tswapong and other formerly vassal peoples living in any district where there was a tribal overseer of one of the major tribes, were obliged to hand over all hunting spoils such as ivory, ostrich feathers and skins. A royal overseer kept such goods for himself, a servant overseer delivered them to the Chief. In 1875 Khama (Ngwato) renounced such tribute; and in 1899 Bathoen (Ngwaketse) allowed the Kgalagadi to sell skins and other products for themselves. However, such forced tribute persisted among the Ngwato and Tawana overseers, with respect to the San, until the late 1930's.

With the disappearance of tribute, by the end of the 1930's people had more freedom connected with hunting than they had previously possessed under customary law, but on the other hand, this freedom began to be restricted by the protection that the Chiefs extended to large game at the request of the Administration. Schapera (1943) considered that the only people seriously affected by such changes were the Kgalagadi and the San, and they, apparently, did a great deal of poaching in so much as they ignored the Chiefs' restrictions, and did not hand over the skins which the Tswana claimed as theirs. As for other tribes, hunting had become less important in the Tswana economy.

Chiefs' Decrees (*Melao*).

The earliest known Chiefs' decrees (*melao*) date to well before the Protectorate Administration, one of the earliest being due to the increased commercial value of ivory, while yet another early one appears to be a response to missionary influence[7]. The excessive exploitation of game by European commercial hunters led to further restrictions, this exploitation being the reason why the Chiefs were so ready to co-operate with the Administration in matters of game protection, for not only had they been witness to what had happened in neighbouring South Africa, but they were already seeing the disappearance of game in their own lands[8]. The known decrees were as follows (Schapera 1938, 1943a,1970; Tabler 1960; Campbell pers. comm.):

Year	Decree	Tribe
c 1815	Ivory the property of the Chief.	Ngwaketse
1856	Hunting prohibited on Sundays.	Kwena
1877	Capture of young ostriches prohibited.	Ngwato

Year	Decree	Tribe
1878	Hunting by European commercial prohibited, sport hunters permitted on personal application to the Chief.	Ngwato
1892	Hunting of giraffe and other big game prohibited without permission of the Chief.	Kwena
	Hunting of ostrich prohibited, but Chief gave permission to hunt cock ostriches.	Ngwaketse
1893	Hunting of elephant, giraffe and eland prohibited without special permission of the Chief.	Ngwaketse
1895	Hunting of giraffe, eland and other big game prohibited without permission of the Chief.	Ngwato
1898	The use of deadfalls, staked pits and trapping on roads prohibited. Hoofed game to be caught only with jackal (iron) traps.	Ngwaketse
1910	Hunting of elephant prohibited without permission of the Chief. Hunting of giraffe, buffalo, eland, rhinoceros and hippopotamus prohibited.	Tawana
1913	Immigrants obliged to obey the Chief's laws concerning the destruction of game. The killing of white storks and secretary birds prohibited. Hyrax and guinea-fowl are totally protected on Serowe Hill.	Ngwato
	"We must no longer kill big game animals".	Ngwaketse
1920	Elephants to be hunted only with the permission of the Chief, and one tusk to be given as tribute.	Tawana
1926	Hunting of big game east of the railway line prohibited. Setting traps in other peoples' fields prohibited.	Kgatla
1936	Sale of lion and leopard skins to traders prohibited.	Kwena
1937	Hunting of giraffe and other Royal Game prohibited without the permission of the Chief.	Tawana

The Tswana claimed rights to ownership of all fur-bearing animals and ostrich feathers, extending this, about 1810, to ivory (Campbell, pers. comm.). Stigand (1913) stated that the Tawana Chief gave very limited permission to people to hunt, except in respect of the smaller and more numerous species such as steenbok, duiker, impala and lechwe. Schapera (1970) informs us that most of these laws were still in force in 1940. The list is undoubtedly incomplete, for the same author records that by 1916 the hunting of large game was universally forbidden, unless authorised by the respective Chief.

Roberts (1969) re-stated Kgatla customary law relating to game in 1967 as follows:

1. No one may hunt on arable land allotted to another in such a way as to interfere with standing crops.

2. The hunting of kudu, impala and springbok was prohibited. (Later this was amended to moderate hunting being permitted).

Statutory Law

When the British Government, at the request of the Tswana Chiefs, assumed jurisdiction over Bechuanaland in 1885, the first Assistant Commissioner was instructed "not to interfere with the Native Administration; the Chiefs are understood not to be desirous of parting with their rights of sovereignty, nor are Her Majesty's Government by any means anxious to assume the responsibilities of it." In May 1891, an Order in Council was issued, authorising the High Commissioner to provide for "the administration of justice, the raising of revenue, and generally for the order and good government of all persons"; but a despatch accompanying the Order directed that jurisdiction should be confined as far as possible to Europeans, leaving the Chiefs and persons living under their tribal authority almost entirely alone (Hailey 1956). The reason why statute law was to be applied only to Europeans (or, more correctly, "foreigners"), has been explained by Pain (1978), for the British Government insisted that, as a protectorate was an independent state, the protecting power was not entitled to exercise jurisdiction over anyone but British subjects in the absence of consent in the relevant treaty as far as the indigenous population was concerned. It was not until 1910 that a Court interpretation of the Foreign Jurisdiction Act, 1890, declared that the Crown had a right to legislate for, and subject to its administration, all of the inhabitants of a protected country.

The Proclamation of the 10th of June 1891 stated that (Sec. 19): "the law to be administered shall, as nearly as circumstances of the country will permit, be the same as the law for the time being in force in the Colony of the Cape of Good Hope: provided that no Act passed after this date by the Parliament of the Colony of the Cape of Good Hope shall be deemed to apply to the said territory". This was clarified by Proclamation 36 of 1909 by referring to "laws" in place of "law", and adding that no statutes promulgated after the reception date were to apply "unless specially applied thereto by Proclamation" (Thompson 1959, Pain 1978).

Concern for game received early attention, perhaps largely as a result of complaints by Major Grey of the Bechuanaland Border Police, who was stationed at Macloutsie. In a letter dated the 21.4.1894, he wrote that between March 1893 and March 1894 members of the Ngwato Tribe sold over 600 heads [head?] of large game; one store at Macloutsie alone buying 348. He considered that the tribesmen were responsible for 90% of animals killed, and urged protection for sable and gemsbok. This letter, sent to the Administrator, Sir Sidney Shippard, was passed to the Assistant Commissioner, the Reverend J.S. Moffat, who replied as follows:

"Palapye
3rd July 1894

Sir,

I have the honour to acknowledge receipt of your letter No. 5 a/c of the ninth of June enclosing one from Major Grey on the subject of the destruction of game in the Protectorate. The question is not by any means a new one. I have long ago discussed the matter with the Chief Khama. He is himself substantially in sympathy with the aims of Major Grey and his people have instructions accordingly.

11

It is only fair however that I should mention certain circumstances which have much discouraged him and his people in any serious attempt to preserve the game. Last year there was a great trek of Boers through the western part of the Bamangwato country, who were on their way to Damaraland via Lake Ngami. These people besides almost coming to blows with the herds at the Bamangwato cattle posts for the possession of the water – also hunted far and wide along their route and destroyed much game including many giraffes.

A man named Van Rooyen, who was at the time living in Tati, made excursions over the Shashe, into what is known as the disputed territory, and killed much game including giraffes. He was warned off by Khama, but not until the mischief had been done. Similar raids have been made over the Crocodile River by Boers from the Transvaal, who when Khama's people objected to their proceedings stated that they were there with the concurrence of the police detachment at Ngwapa. The police authorities have since denied this. I give these statements on Khama's authority as derived from his people and of course I do not vouch for their absolute correctness, but the effect is the same. Even with the Proclamation of September 19th last, there is much difficulty in enforcing the law. I think it is right to state all this to show or to account for the attitude of the native mind and for a certain amount of apathy on questions of this kind, but I repeat that Khama himself is in sympathy with the spirit of Major Grey's remarks: and is so far as in him lies carrying out a policy tending to a moderate preservation of the game."

Subsequent to this, the Assistant Commissioner at Gaborone, W.H. Surmon, approached the Chiefs Sebele (Kwena), Bathoen (Ngwaketse) and Linchwe (Kgatla), on the subject in September 1894, receiving written replies from Sebele and Bathoen. Chief Linchwe informed Surmon verbally that his people only killed game for food and [he] would be glad if no new law was made on the subject. In a letter dated the 27.9.1894 to Chief Bathoen, Surmon asked that a close season be observed, and that there be complete protection of elephant, eland, giraffe, gemsbok and sable; also young or half-grown animals and females. Bathoen replied that the species no longer occurred in his area. Sebele answered by letter of the 1.10.1894 as follows [translation]:

"It has been my wish for some years that a close season should be observed re species of rare game ... My people, the true Bakwena, do not agree with my ideas on the subject and have already said that my ideas are far too strict re game. But with your assistance I shall really do my best in this matter."

As a result of his representations, Surmon wrote to Sir Francis Newton, Colonial Secretary at Vryburg, as follows (4.10.1894):

"I think it would not be advisable to make any alterations in the game law at present and that it would be better to request the Chiefs to carry out His Honour's proposals amongst their own people as far as practicable in their own territories." (BNA S. 159/4).

Hence, in a letter from the British Colonial Office of the 7th of November 1895, to the Chiefs Kgama, Sebele and Bathoen, which laid the foundations of the Protectorate (Sillery 1952), it was stated:

'Outside of the boundaries now laid down for the Chiefs, the British South Africa Company will administer; but the Chiefs will continue to have the hunting rights which they now enjoy, provided that they agree to observe a "close season" and that they will nominate certain hunters for each year, to whom hunting licences will be issued by the proper authority."

The rights thus appeared to be conditional, but the Chiefs did not query the provisos in their reply, and they seem never to have been insisted upon. Neither did they query the ambiguity of the statement which could be interpreted as referring only to hunting outside of the tribal boundaries, but it has always seemingly been construed as referring to hunting within the tribal territories, becoming the foundation for the tribal hunting legislation which, instituted in 1967 after

Independence, remained in force until 1979 when all hunting legislation was finally amalgamated.

As a result of the 1891 Proclamation, the first statutory game law to be applied to the Protectorate was Act No. 36 of the 6th July 1886 of the Colony of the Cape of Good Hope, titled "For the Better Preservation of Game", and cited as the "Game Law Amendment Act, 1886", since it replaced earlier acts of 1822 and 1823. At the same time, Act No. 24 of 1884, "The Ostrich Export Duty Act", also came into force.

Synopsis of the Principal Enactments[9]

1891 The Game Law Amendment Act, 1886 (Appendix I) introduced the following principles:

i. restriction on the hunting of certain species of wild animals termed "game", which were defined. They included the quagga, which had been extinct for 28 years (Sec. 2).

ii. Close seasons were introduced, during which period of the year animals could not be hunted (Sec. 3).

iii. Licences were required to hunt, capture or sell, game (Sec. 4).

iv. Exception to the law requiring a licence could be made where animals were damaging crops or gardens, but the burden of proof lay with the accused (Sec. 4).

v. No hunting could take place on private land without the landowner's permission (Sec. 7).

vi. A landowner could declare, by notice published in the Gazette, or in a newspaper, that he wished to protect game on his land; in which case a person could be fined for hunting on such land without the owner's permission (Sec. 7).

vii. The eggs and young of game species could be collected under permit for rearing or breeding, acclimatisation, or for scientific investigation (Sec. 6).

viii. Nominated species could be protected from hunting for up to three years in any specified area (Sec.11).

ix. A reward, equal to half of the fine imposed, was to be paid to a person whose information led to the prosecution (Sec.10).

x. A landowner did not require a licence to hunt on his own land (Sec.16).

The "Ostrich Export Duty Act, 1884", imposed a tax on the export of ostriches and ostrich eggs except to any neighbouring country which had also imposed an export tax of like value (Sec.1).

1893 Proclamation of the 19th September (Appendix II). This, the first Protectorate Proclamation concerning game, did not repeal the Game Law Amendment Act, but implemented its provisions for licensing and the payment of fees. The principal points were:

i. "game" was re-defined as "Large Game", namely the wild ostrich, hippopotamus, rhinoceros, buffalo, zebra, quagga "and all animals of the Antelope species, except Eland, Duiker and Steinbok". Elephant and giraffe were not included in this definition (Sec. 2).

ii. Licences for hunting parties of not more than five persons could be issued for

13

tribal areas with the consent of the Chief or Chiefs concerned (Sec. 3).

iii. Licences were not transferable, and were valid for one year only (Sec. 4).

iv. A licence fee was specified, of which 25% went to the Chief (Sec. 5).[10]

v. The close season was defined as from the 1st of September to the last day of February (Sec.6)[11].

vi. Elephant, giraffe and eland, were specially protected (Sec. 7).

vii. The fine for hunting without a licence was increased from 200 shillings to 3,000 shillings, and penalties could be recovered by seizure of property (Sec. 8 & 9).

viii. Officials could be issued free permits ("Station permits") for use within 48 kms' radius of their station. Officials travelling on duty and persons travelling on "ordinary roads" could hunt for food without a licence (Sec. 11).

ix. The provisions of this Proclamation did not apply to members of any tribe killing large game, elephants, giraffes or eland, within their own Tribal Territory (Sec. 13).

1904 The Large Game Preservation Proclamation (No. 22), repealed the 1893 Proclamation. The definition of Large Game was amended to exclude eland and to include rhebuck and klipspringer under antelope species. Also:

i. Licence fees were revised and issued for periods of two weeks to more than three months (Sec. 5).

ii. Special permits could be issued *gratis* for elephant, giraffe and eland (Sec. 9).

iii. The Station permit was dropped and replaced with an open permit.

iv. Ration permits could be issued during the close season (Sec. 13).

v. Exception for tribal members was limited to those killing large game, elephant, giraffe or eland "with the permission of the Paramount Chief" (Sec. 14), but no person "whether native or otherwise" could kill the hen bird of the ostrich or "remove, interfere with, disturb or be in possession of the feathers or eggs of such birds without the permission of the Resident Commissioner" (Sec. 15).

1907 Proclamation No. 2 instituted Section 11 of the Act of 1886, empowering the High Commissioner to protect species in specified areas for up to three years at a time. Proclamation No. 3 exempted tribal members from Proclamation No. 2.

Proclamation No. 39 repealed the Ostrich Export Duty Act of 1884, making unlawful the export of any ostrich or ostrich egg except to those countries which also prohibited export. These were defined by High Commissioner's Notices as Cape Colony, the Transvaal, Natal, Basutoland, Swaziland (Notice 130 of 1907); Southern Rhodesia (Notice 21 of 1908); Orange River Colony (Notice 75 of 1908); Mozambique (Notice 104 of 1908) and German South West Africa (Notice 58 of 1909). It was repealed by Act No. 7 of 1966.

1911 Proclamation No. 42 instituted a licence to trade in game products. Exemption was made for landowners trading in game products derived from their own land and for tribesmen in tribal areas. The burden of proof that any game had not been exported for sale, or that any game traded or exported, had not been killed within the Protectorate, lay with the accused. This was intended to control trade in small game which was not protected under Proc. 22 of 1904, game being defined as: rhebuck, klipspringer, duiker, steinbuck, hare, wild goose, wild duck, snipe, pauw, black korhaan, Vaal korhaan, bush korhaan, dikkop, guinea-fowl, pheasant, partridge, grouse and plover.

1914 Proclamation No.44, Plumage Birds Protection and Preservation, defined wild birds as any wild birds not defined as game birds, and made it an offence to trade in, or export, the plumage of any wild birds not ordinarily used as articles of diet; to hunt, capture or possess such wild birds; to trade in, possess, remove or destroy the eggs of such wild birds, without a permit. A permit could be issued where the requirement was for scientific or educational purposes. HCN No. 63 excluded cock ostriches from these provisions. This Proclamation, repealed by Act No. 36 of 1967, appears to have exploited a loophole in the 1895 agreement, by legislating for species not considered as "game", and thereby making no exceptions for tribesmen.

1924 High Commissioner's Notice No. 20 protected Large Game for a period of one year in all Crown Land north of the Molopo River. This was the first application of Section 11 of the Act of 1886 (replaced by Sec. 5 of Proc. 17 of 1925). The definition implied the whole of Botswana, and in 1926 it was re-defined as "northwards to the 24th parallel of south latitude" (HCN No. 18) (See Part II). In 1931 Small Game was included in the definition for the first time (HCN No. 33).

1925 Proclamation No. 17, the Bechuanaland Protectorate Game Proclamation, was one of the principal enactments, repealing the Act of 1886 and its eleven subsequent active Proclamations, excluding the Plumage Birds Protection and Preservation Proclamation. It instituted the following amendments to existing law:

  i. game was further defined as "Royal Game", "Large Game" and "Small Game" (Sec. 2).
  ii. The hunting of Royal Game was forbidden except on special licence (Sec. 14 & 15).
  iii. The licence required for trade in game products was applied to landowners except in respect of Small Game killed on their own land (Sec.16).
  iv. The exemption of tribesmen to the provisions of the Proclamation did not apply to trade in giraffe products (Sec. 23), when Section 22 applied: "No person shall receive or deal in under any pretext whatsoever the hides or tails of the giraffe without the permission in writing of the Resident Commissioner". Section 30 stipulated that a member of a tribe "may be in possession of the hides or tails of giraffe lawfully hunted within such territory" (i.e. the territory lawfully hunted by such tribe)

1929 Proclamation No. 48 placed the burden of proof on the accused to prove that any game in his possession was not hunted in contravention of the law.

1930 Proclamation No. 27 introduced the forfeiture of any firearms and ammunition found in the possession of an accused at the time of the commission of an offence of unlawful hunting: "the Court may in addition to any other penalty imposed order the confiscation of any firearms and ammunition ..."

1932 High Commissioner's Notice No. 53 instituted an important new protected area, protecting both Large and Small Game for a period of three years in an estimated 15,550 km2 (6,000 sq miles) in Chobe District. This area, which encompassed the present Chobe National Park, was increased the following year to an estimated 20,740 km2 (8,000 sq miles) (HCN No. 139 of 1933). The Notice was continued until 1943 (see Part II).

1934 Proclamation No.74, Native Administration Proclamation, empowered the Administration to issue, through the Chiefs, any order thought desirable "for the protection and preservation of game" (Sec. 17(1)(k)[12]. Few orders relating to game were issued under this Proclamation, these being HCN No's 44 of 1938; 108 of 1940; 42, 189 of 1941; 274 of 1942 and 115 of 1947. Schapera interprets this as being due to the fact that the existing customary law was adequate, but states that Notices no's 108 of 1940 and 42 of 1941 were both published after consultation with the tribes concerned; and we may suppose that this applied to the other Notices also.

1940 Proclamation No. 19, the Bechuanaland Protectorate Game Proclamation, repealed No. 17 of 1925 and its amendments, and introduced a number of important new provisions in conformity with the 1933 London Convention. The principal new provisions were:

i. empowering legislation for the creation of Game Reserves and Sanctuaries (Sec. 5 & 6); provision for the appointment of Game Rangers to control them (Sec. 28), and provision for the drawing-up of regulations covering their protection and control (Sec. 29). A permit could be issued to hunt in a game reserve or sanctuary for scientific or administrative purposes, or "when the presence of that animal or bird is detrimental to the purposes of the Game Reserve or Sanctuary" (Sec. 14(2) (b).

ii. The definition of "game" included game products (Sec. 2(1)).

iii. The following methods of hunting were declared unlawful (Sec.12):

– hunting between half an hour after sunset and half an hour before sunrise;
– hunting from an aeroplane or motor vehicle;
– surrounding an animal by fire;
– using dazzling lights or flares.

iv. A European member of the Bechuanaland Protectorate Police could arrest without warrant persons suspected of possessing game or game products illegally (Sec.11).

v. An export fee was introduced for the export of meat in excess of 9kg, but a tribesman received the permit *gratis* if he was in possession of a certificate from his Chief recommending such export. This provision did not apply to landowners killing game on their own land (Sec. 16).

vi. Written permission was required for the export of ivory, rhinoceros horn, hippopotamus tusks, skins and trophies, specifying a gazetted Port of Exit. Ivory and rhinoceros horn was to be marked with a code (Sec. 18).

vii. Any Justice of the Peace or European member of the BP Police could search without a warrant in connection with (v) and (vi) above (Sec. 19).

viii. "Government trophies" were introduced. That is, all unclaimed game found dead, game accidentally killed or game killed in defence of any person, on Crown land, and all unclaimed ivory and trophies found on Crown land, was the property of the Administration (Sec. 26).

ix. A Small Game licence fee was introduced, and a 7-day licence for residents and non-residents. The holder of a Large Game licence could hunt Small Game with the same licence (Sec. 8). A Royal Game Licence could be issued *gratis* (a fee had been introduced by Proc. 12 of 1932), but a fee scale was retained (Sec. 15).

x. A number of species was added to the Large and Small Game Schedules, and additions made to the Royal Game Schedule. The quagga, which had now been extinct for 77 years, was finally dropped from the Schedule of protected species.

High Commisioners' notice No. 42 extended the area protected under HCN No. 27 of 1930, by including "the whole of the Kgalagadi District". For the first time a proviso was added to the effect that permits could be issued to native residents of the area to hunt and kill game "in reasonable quantities for food", although in fact permits had been issued since 1931 (Resident Commissioner to J.F. Ludorf, Chairman of the South African National Parks Board, 1938, BNA S.108/2/2; and see Note 13). The qualification, which was not directed at Remote Area Dwellers, was dropped in 1952 (HCN No. 57).

High Commissioner's Notice No.107 established the first Game Reserve under Proc. 19 of 1940, along the Nossop River.

1950 High Commissioner's Notice No. 228 brought into force the Laws of Bechuanaland, Game becoming Chapter 114. This law consolidated the amendments enacted since 1940 and introduced the following:

– Proc. 25 of 1944 became universal (Sec. 14(2)(c)).

– The right of search upon suspicion without a warrant was extended to the owner or occupier of any land, or his European agent; and to any European Police Officer. Obstruction was an offence (Sec. 19(bis)).

– It became an offence to convey a firearm, not secured or in a case, along any road where game was, or was likely to be, by anyone not having the right to hunt on such land (Sec. 24(2)).

– The fine for hunting on private land without the owner's permission was increased 7.5 times, with the possibility of both fine and imprisonment.

The Wild Birds Protection Proclamation, 1914, became Chapter 115.

1952 Proclamation No. 3 amended Cap. 114 and introduced the following:

i. extension of the close season from the beginning of August in place of October (Sec.1).

ii. A separate licence for Small Game was required (Sec. 2(b)).

iii. Forfeiture was widened to include "animal, vehicle or aeroplane" (Sec. 3(a)).

iv. The use of a motor vehicle or aeroplane to locate game for hunting, drive game from private land or aerodromes, or for hunting on private land by the owner or an authorised person, was deleted (Sec. 4).

v. Hunting game in the Tuli Block during the close season for "domestic purposes" was amended to "such conditions as shall be approved" (Sec. 5).

vi. A landowner was no longer exempted from requiring a licence to export small game meat taken on his own land (Sec. 16(1)).

vii. Trespass with intent with a firearm on any land where game was, or was likely to be, was an offence, and the fine was further increased (Sec. 7).

viii. Any police officer, owner or occupier, or, in the case of Crown lands, a District Officer or Justice of the Peace, was empowered to demand the particulars of any person in possession of a firearm or other device, or accompanied by a dog, and to order such person to quit the land, failure to comply being an offence (Sec. 7).

ix. The owner or occupier of any land with game on it, or having the shooting rights, was empowered to destroy any dog not used in lawful hunting which was pursuing, or in search of, any game on such land (Sec. 7).

1960 High Commissioner's Notice No. 65 established the Chobe Game Reserve, protection of the area having lapsed since 1943.

1961 Proclamation No. 22, the Fauna Conservation Proclamation, was an extensive, completely revised legislation for "further and better provision of the conservation and control of the wild animal life of the Territory and to give effect to the International Convention of 1933, as amended, for the protection of the fauna and flora of African", repealing Cap. 114 and forming the basis for current law. The previous 30 sections were increased to 95, introducing the following:

i. licensing officers and honorary Game Officers (Sec. 89).

ii. Private Game Reserves (Sec. 10).

iii. Controlled Hunting Areas (Sec. 10).

iv. Landholder's privileges were defined as to ownership of the land (Sec. 16).

v. Licences were restricted to bird, general game and supplementary game, the latter being additional to the general game licence or for persons entitled to landholder's privileges (Sec. 17,18,19, 20).

vi. Maintenance of a register of species taken on licences and permits was obligatory (Sec. 39).

vii. A professional guide [hunter] required a licence to operate (Sec. 28).

viii. Persons convicted of game laws in adjacent territories were not eligible for a hunting licence (Sec. 32).

ix. Permits could be issued for the killing or driving of game for the control of disease, the tcitling of animals in the interests of public safety, or for the protection of livestock, crops, water installations or fences (Sec. 35).

x. The protection of animals in a defined area was restricted to one year for the control of the spread of disease, protection of life or property, or for administrative purposes (Sec. 38).

xi. Owners or occupiers could destroy on their land any animal causing damage, but the trophies were the property of the Administration, or of the African Authority in the case of Tribal land, and the meat could be consumed but not sold. The burden of proof that the animal was causing damage lay with the person killing the animal (Sec. 41).

xii. Any person could kill or injure any animal in self-defence, or in the protection of others, the same conditions as in (xi) above applying (Sec. 43).

xiii. Animals killed by accident or in error must be reported (Sec. 44).

xiv. No person could take any animal on any land without the written permission of the owner or occupier (Sec. 45).

xv. The burden of proof lay with the accused found on any land in possession of any weapon or other means of taking an animal, to prove that he was not intending to hunt (Sec. 46).

xvi. Owners or occupiers of private land could not give permission to hunt thereon unless the hunter was in possession of a licence or permit (Sec. 49). In the case of Tribal land the African Authority gave permission (Sec. 50).

xvii. Persons entitled to landholder's privileges could hunt during the close season (Sec. 55 (2) (a));

xviii. Any person wounding an animal must take all reasonable steps to kill it, and the wounding of dangerous animals must be reported, even by witnesses (Sec. 51).

xix. Hunting or capture by night, or with a dazzling light, could be allowed under permit (Sec. 54 (2)).

xx. Unlawful methods of hunting included:
   – discharging a firearm at any game animal from a vehicle, mechanically propelled vessel or aircraft (Sec. 56 (1));
   – capturing with a vessel or aircraft; but this did not apply to persons with landholder's privileges nor, if a permit was granted, to driving animals from an airstrip (Sec. 56 (2)).

xi. The use or possession of poisoned bait, poisoned weapons, pitfalls, stakes, nets, gins, traps, set guns, missiles containing explosives, snares, fences or enclosures, was prohibited (Sec. 57).

xxii. Baboon, black-backed jackal, hyaena and hunting dog, were declared vermin and could be hunted without restriction (Sec. 58).

xxiii. Restrictions on sale were extended to eggs, hides and skins (Sec. 60).

xxiv. It was an offence to purchase game animals or game products unless the seller had a valid permit to sell. The special provision concerning giraffe was dropped (Sec. 61).

xxv. A trophy dealer's licence was instituted (Sec. 65 (3)), and a register of transactions was required to be maintained and returns made (Sec. 67).

xxvi. Ivory and rhinoceros horn must be produced to an authorised officer (Sec. 68), weighed, and a certificate of ownership issued (Sec. 69). All existing ivory and rhinoceros horn had to be registered (Sec. 71) and all imports (Sec. 72).

xxvii. Unregistered ivory or rhinoceros horn could not be transferred (Sec. 73), and elephant tusks below a prescribed weight were Government trophies (Sec. 75 (e)).

xxviii. Presumptions embraced a game animal in, or upon, any vehicle, boat or aircraft, or at any camping place, presumed to be in the possession of the persons upon, or in, or in any way connected with, the foregoing (Sec. 80 (3));
   – the burden of proving any fact which would be a defence to a charge of contravention of the Proclamation, or to any Regulations, lay with the person so charged (Sec. 80 (5));
   – any flesh, hide or skin was presumed to be that of a game animal unless proved to the contrary, and any species of game animal was presumed to be that species unless the contrary was proved (Sec. 80 (6));
   – any unlawful act was presumed to have been committed upon certain land unless the contrary was proved (Sec. 80 (6));
   – where it was unlawful to take a certain sex of animal, if the distinguishing features had been removed, then the animal was presumed to be that sex which it was unlawful to take (Sec. 80 (8));
   – failure to report any matter or to deliver any article or thing was presumed to be intended (Sec. 80 (10));
   – any person found on any land at night without permission, and in possession of any dazzling light and means of taking animals, was presumed to have hunted (Sec. 80 (11));
   – conveying an animal at night without a licence or permit presumes that the animal was hunted at night (Sec. 80 (12));
   – failure of a driver to stop a vehicle presumes that the registered owner was driving at that time (Sec. 80 (14)).

xxix. Records made by authorised persons are prima facie evidence Sec. 80 (13)).

xxx. Powers were granted to policemen, game officers and game scouts. Where an offence was believed to have been committed, authorised officers could enter on any land and request the production of a licence or other authority and, except in a township, could search without a warrant; but game scouts were excluded from entering a dwelling house without a warrant. Authorised officers could destroy any pitfall, gin, trap, snare or similar contrivance (Sec. 81); and policemen and game officers could enter the premises of trophy dealers (Sec. 82).

xxxi. Any game officer or game scout, in uniform, had the right to stop any person or vehicle (Sec. 83).

xxxii. A game officer could erect road barriers, and it was an offence not to stop at such barrier (Sec. 84).

xxxiii. Forfeiture was extended to any article or thing used in connection with an offence, and the discretionary cancellation of any licence, permit, or other authorisation, was added if the offence carried a maximum fine of less than Rand 200 (Sec. 85 (1)).

Where the offence was one of hunting upon and without the owner's consent or of hunting at night, or for any other offence with a maximum fine of more than Rand 200, forfeiture of any weapon or animal used in the commission of the offence, and the cancellation of any licence, permit, or other authorisation, was mandatory (Sec. 85 (2),(3)); but forfeiture of any vehicle was discretionary (Sec. 85 (3)). If the Resident Commissioner was satisfied that the items were not the property of the person convicted, and the owner was unable to prevent their use by the person so convicted, then he could order their return (Sec. 85 (3)).

xxxiv. A person found not guilty of the offence as charged, but guilty of another, could be found guilty of the other offence although not charged with it (Sec. 87).

xxxv. Any game officer or game scout, with the consent of the owner or occupier of any land, was empowered to destroy on such land any animal which had caused, or was causing, or was likely to cause, damage to any livestock, crops, water installation or fence; and a game officer could destroy a dog found hunting on land other than private land, if not in the keeping of, or accompanied by, a person lawfully on such land (Sec. 88).

xxxvi. Impersonation of an officer was an offence (Sec. 91).

xxxvii. The power to make regulations was widened in scope and included controlled Hunting Areas, the capture and care of animals, and the sale of traps (Sec. 93).

xxxviii. The list of Royal Game was increased with the addition of cheetah, Chobe bushbuck, waterbuck, hippopotamus, klipspringer, oribi and rhebok; but birds were removed and the elephant was limited to immature specimens and females. The former Large and Small Game classifications were changed to Game Birds (greatly restricted as to species), and Game Licence Animals (mature males only).

xxxix. Dangerous animals were defined by species.

The Proclamation bore the customary proviso that it did not apply to Africans in their Tribal Territories, with the exceptions of the section applying to export or import (Sec . 62), and that of dealing in trophies (Sec. 65),(Sec. 4).

High Commissioner's Notice No. 33 established the Central Kalahari Game Reserve.

1967 Act No. 47, the Fauna Conservation (Amendment) Act, while retaining the majority of Proc. 22 of 1961, introduced the following principal amendments:

i. the category of Royal Game became "Conserved animal" (Sec. 12).

ii. A category of "protected game" was introduced (Sec. 12).

iii. Section 4, excluding Africans on Crown land from the application, was deleted and replaced with exclusion only from "land proclaimed a National Park" (Sec. 4).

iv. Provision was made for Remote Area Dwellers by the addition of a section to the effect that "Subject to the provisions of any regulation to the contrary regulating the terms and conditions of hunting within a controlled hunting area" exempting persons "entirely dependent ... on hunting and gathering veld produce ... where the animal is hunted for the reasonable food requirements of the hunter or of the members of the community to which he belongs" from the provisions of the Act, except for conserved animals (Sec. 4 (3)).

v. Remote Area Dwellers were allowed to use "poisoned weapon, pitfall, stake, trap, snare, fence or enclosure" and also to possess poisoned weapons, traps or snares; but not traps or snares "of a type manufactured for commercial purposes or a wire snare, fence or enclosure" (Sec. 15).

vi. Regulations governing controlled hunting areas were provided for (Sec. 5).

vii. The distinction exempting Africans in Tribal Territories or on Crown land from the restrictions on purchasing game and game products, was removed (Sec. 17).

viii. A curio-maker's licence was introduced (Sec. 23).

ix. Hunting in Forest Reserves required a permit issued by a Forest Officer (Sec. 25).

x. A permit was required to possess a captive animal (Sec. 25).

xi. The Chobe Game Reserve was deleted from the Schedule of protected areas, but the boundaries were not repealed. (This was not done until 1980 (S.I No. 125)).

Act. No. 48, the National Parks Act, was introduced for "the establishment of National Parks and for the preservation of wild animal and fish life; vegetation and objects of scientific interest; and to provide for the control and management of such Parks and for matters incidental thereto". This Act declared the Chobe National Park.

Statutory Instrument No.64 promulgated the first Tribal Territory hunting regulations, for the Bamangwato Tribe hunting on the Tribal Territory, made by the Minister "after consultation with the Tribal Authority[14] of the Bamangwato Tribal Territory and the appropriate District Council". The main provisions were:

i. a schedule of "tribal game" was introduced.

ii. The hunting of protected game (Reg. 4), and tribal game (Reg. 5), required a licence.

iii. Certain species could be hunted without a licence Reg. 6).

iv. A close season was defined (Reg. 7).

v. Licensing officers were appointed by the Tribal Authority (Reg. 8 (1)).

vi. Fees were set for licences payable to the District Council (Reg. 9(4),(5)).

vii. Licences were not transferable (Reg. 9 (6)).

viii. Destruction of animals in self-defence was allowed, the burden of proof lying with the person killing the animal (Reg. 10).

ix. The occupier of any land or his authorised member could destroy on such land any animal causing damage to any livestock, crops, water installation or fence (Reg. 11 (2)).

x. Written permission of the Tribal Authority was required for the use of poisoned bait, metal trap, set gun or wire snare, except where other than poisoned bait was used in the immediate vicinity of any enclosure in which livestock were kept (Reg. 12). No exemption was made for Remote Area Dwellers.

In 1970 these regulations were amended (S.I. No. 32) as follows:

i. Licences could be transferred among family members if endorsed with the transferee's name (Reg. 4 (b)).

ii. Only one type of licence could be issued per season per holder (Reg. 4 (c)).

iii. Every licence must bear a register of the animals killed (Reg. 4(c)).

iv. The licence must be produced when trophies were disposed of (Reg. 7).

v. The sale of live animals was prohibited (Reg. 7).

vi. Trophies of animals killed in self-defence or damaging property belonged to the District Council (Reg. 6).

vii. Hunting at night by means of a dazzling light was prohibited (Reg .7).

viii. Chasing with, or shooting from, a vehicle, was prohibited (Reg. 7).

ix. Chasing or hunting using a horse, mule or donkey, was prohibited (Reg. 7).

x. The wounding of dangerous animals must be reported (Reg. 7).

xi. The eggs of all birds were conserved (Reg.9).

xii. A person convicted under the Regulations automatically forfeited his licence and was disqualified from holding one for 12 months (Reg. 8).

1968 Statutory Instrument No. 4 announced the first Controlled Hunting Areas, in the Kweneng District. This was followed by Regulations (S.I No. 7) which, among other provisions:

– did not apply to members of the Bakwena Tribe;
– set quotas for each species in each area.

Statutory Instrument No.13 exempted Remote Area Dwellers from the Batawana Tribal Territory Hunting Regulations (S.I. No. 65 of 1967), which were similar to S.I. No. 64 of 1967 except that a fee was introduced for certain categories, and the outsider's fee changed. Statutory Instrument No.15 declared Controlled Hunting Areas on State land, and S.I. No. 17 provided regutations which specified:

i. a resident of the area could hunt certain species of small game without a licence or permit (Reg. 4).

ii. A licence or permit was required for hunting (Reg. 3), except by a public officer on duty hunting other than conserved animals (Reg. 4 (c)).

iii. Quotas were to be set (Reg. 6).

No exemption was made for Remote Area Dwellers, who were thus restricted to hunting small game.

Statutory Instrument No. 23 provided regulations for hunting in Controlled Hunting Areas on Tribal land. These regulations did not apply to members of a tribe hunting in the Tribal Territory of such tribe, but otherwise were similar to the regulations for State land (S.I. No. 17 of 1968). No provision was made for Remote Area Dwellers.

Statutory Instrument No.37 provided hunting regulations for the Bakwena Tribal Territory. Exemption was provided for Remote Area Dwellers (Reg. 13), otherwise the regulations were similar to S.l. .No. 64 of 1967. S.I. No. 56 provided similar regulations for the Bangwaketse Tribal Territory, without provision for Remote Area Dwellers. In both cases, fees were introduced for all licences.

1971 Statutory Instrument No.83 created the Gemsbok National Park, with an area of 24,000km2, although the Game Reserve (HCN No.107 of 1940) was not formally de-gazetted.

1973 Statutory Instrument No. 106 provided hunting regulations for the Bakgatla Tribal Territory. These were similar to other tribal regulations and no exemption was made for Remote Area Dwellers.

1976 Statutory Instrument No. 160, the Law Revision Order,1976, redesignated the Fauna Proclamation, 1961, as the Fauna Conservation Act, Cap. 38. 01 of the Laws of Botswana. The National Parks Act,1967, became Cap. 38. 03. The Fauna Conservation Act incorporated the revisions from 1961, and the area described as a Game Reserve under HCN No. 107 of 1940 was dropped from the Schedule of Game Reserve and Sanctuaries (First Schedule).

1979 Act No. 1 amended the Fauna Conservation Act. There was a number of important changes:

   i. the provision granting exemption to the hunting law to members of a tribe hunting on the Tribal Territory was deleted, and references to the Chief, Tribe or Tribal Authority, were replaced by the Land Board.
   ii. Provision for Remote Area Dwellers to hunt on State land was limited to permitting the Minister to make regulations allowing "the hunting of any animal, other than a conserved animal, in any area by persons resident in that area who are principally dependent for their living on hunting and gathering veld produce" (Sec. 4 (b)).
   iii. Provision was made for fees in respect of Game Reserve or National Parks on Tribal land to be paid to the relevant Land Boards or District Councils, up to an amount paid to central government for that year (Sec. 6).
   iv. Non-residents could not hunt without being accompanied by a professional hunter (Sec. 7 (a)).
   v. Wildlife Management Areas were defined and rules for their control outlined (Sec. 7 (b)).
   vi. Citizens could hunt unscheduled animals for consumption (Sec. 9 (a)).
   vii. Landholder's privileges were limited to citizens or residents, or to those entitled by declaration of the Minister, and certain species were restricted as to the number which could be hunted (Sec. 10).
   viii. A landholder could, "for his own profit, with the approval of the Chief Game Warden" authorise others to hunt on his land if they were in possession of a licence to hunt (Sec. 10).
   ix. General and supplementary game licences were replaced with "Single" and "Small" game licences (Sec. 11).
   x. Game licences could be transferred on "such terms and conditions as may be prescribed" (Sec. 14).
   xi. The section permitting the destruction of "any animal causing damage to any livestock, crops, water installation or fence", was replaced with the words "threatens to cause, causes or is causing damage" (Sec. 18).
   xii. A licensing officer was empowered to issue a certificate of ownership for trophies of animals destroyed causing damage and a permit for sale of the

meat, but not for animals killed threatening to cause damage (Sec. 18).

xiii. No compensation could be paid to a person who had the right to destroy an animal but failed to do so, unless it was a predator which escaped into a protected area after killing livestock, or, in the case of an elephant, it was killed and the trophy surrendered (Sec. 18).

xiv. Failure to report the destruction of an animal causing damage was an offence (Sec. 18).

xv. A person entitled to landholder's privileges could not use a vehicle, aircraft or powered boat to hunt with (Sec. 22).

xvi. Hunting was allowed only with a rifle, shotgun or dog (Sec. 23).

xvii. The category of vermin was repealed (Sec. 24).

xviii. The curio-maker's licence was repealed, this being covered by the trophy-dealer's licence (Sec. 24).

xix. Government trophies in tribal areas other than in a Game Reserve or National Park were the property of the Land Board and not of the Tribe (Sec. 32).

xx. Officers were empowered to enter and search within a township, and game scouts and game guards could search a dwelling house without a warrant (Sec. 37).

xxi. Game guards were accorded similar powers to game officers and game scouts (Sec. 36, 37).

xxii. Forfeitures could be claimed as another's property within 90 days in place of 28 days (Sec. 40).

xxiii. More species were added to the list of conserved animals (Second Schedule).

Statutory Instrument No. 18 abolished separate regulations for each tribal area, the Fauna Conservation (Unified Hunting) Regulations,1979, embodying a single set of regulations applicable throughout Botswana. The principal changes were:

i. A Special Game Licence was introduced for Remote Area Dwellers, permitting limited free hunting throughout the year of designated species (Reg. 7).

ii. A person could assist another, whom he was hunting with, to kill an animal (Reg. 11).

iii. Licences could be transferred to another citizen with the authorisation of the licensing officer (Reg.12).

iv. Hunting of elephant or buffalo was only allowed with a rifle of minimum specified calibre (Reg. 18).

v. Elephant tusks of less than 11kg weight were Government trophies (Reg. 19). (Amended by S.I. No. 31 to 10kg).

vi. In addition to the register, a hunting card had to be maintained, listing the animals killed or wounded (Reg. 20).

vii. No one could hunt unless accompanied by a game officer, game scout, game guard or authorised escort, unless authorised to do so by a licensing officer (Reg. 21).

With the promulgation of these regulations, the imposition of a universal game law was essentially complete.

Penalties

At the Chief's Court, Kanye, in 1919 an offender was fined an ox for killing a hartebeest; and in 1937 six offenders were each fined two head of cattle for killing an eland. In the Chief's Tribunal at Molepolole (1935), an offender was fined 10 head of cattle for killing more eland than he was allowed to by the Chief (quoted by Schapera 1943). At this period, the maximum penalty under statute law was a fine of 3,000 shillings; but after Independence, when the statute law became universal (although under separate Tribal Regulations), penalties were reduced significantly to 50 Rand equivalent to about 500 shillings. In 1982 this was increased to Pula 200, about 1300 shillings in today's terms, still below the value of the offence as seen under customary law. Since Independence penalties awarded for offences against the game laws have generally been light. A notable exception was the conviction of four persons in 1971 for hunting without a licence a large number of animals in the Makgadikgadi Pans Game Reserve, who were fined and forfeited a truck, two Land Rover Station Wagons and four firearms (see State vs. Mosinyi & Others, 1972 for appeal). A general reticence of magistrates to award significant penalties, however, has led to the exceptional measure of repeated injunctions from the Chief Justice to apply realistic penalties in line with the economic value of game. For example: "... it is quite obvious therefore that to fine an accused person R10 or R15 for hunting and killing an animal such as an eland is quite unrealistic and only represents a fraction of the commercial value of the animal killed ..." (RM2 RM22 of the 9.9.1976). Compare this with the 12 head of cattle forfeited in 1937!

In 1981 the Chief Justice was obliged to once more draw the attention of the Magistrates' Courts to the leniency of penalties (JC No. 2 of the 30.12.1981). In his review of the case of State vs. Gabaitumele Modibetsane & Gareotelwe Modibetsane, the Chief Justice stated that the fine of Pula 30 imposed by the Magistrate for being in possession of the fresh meat and skin of a kudu, was "totally inadequate": "I will only say that, in future, all Magistrates must look on such cases with more severity ... the State views breaches of this Act with great concern as wildlife is one of Botswana's important natural resources" (BLR 1982(1)). But yet again in 1985 he was obliged to state: "I would reiterate ... and would add that any fines imposed should be considerably more severe than they are at present and should, in all cases be coupled with a term of imprisonment (RM64 I(63) of the 23.12.1985).

In 1986 accused persons were fined Pula 60 for killing a hartebeest without a licence, on two separate occasions. We see that in 1929, when game was much more plentiful, they could have been fined an ox, with a value of about 73 shillings, for the same offence. Probably about twelve times the value of the penalty awarded in 1986. During 1987, however, the maximum fine of Pula 200, plus six months' imprisonment (with four months' suspended), was awarded on five occasions for the killing of a hartebeest without a licence. In two other cases the addition of forfeiture brought the penalty to a value of about Pula 550. But at Maun, two accused were each sentenced to six months' imprisonment, wholly suspended for three years, for killing a giraffe, a conserved animal which had been protected by the Tawana chiefs since the beginning of the century.

It is difficult to make comparisons in economic terms, but since the introduction of a penalty of a 30 shillings fine for hunting without a licence in 1891 (for non-tribesmen only), penalties have been reviewed only three times in 97 years. Figure 1 shows the maximum penalty for hunting without a licence, divided by the minimum rate of tax. That is to say, the penalty is expressed as the number of times the minimum rate of tax shown on a logarithmic scale. The trend shows that, beginning in 1958, when tax rose by 44%, the value of the penalty has shown a sharp decline until, after having exceeded the minimum tax for 85 years, it then dropped below this level. The tax scale is that paid by the indigenous inhabitants, which began as a hut tax in 1899, became a poll tax in 1907, a graded tax in 1949 (Hailey 1953), and finally an income tax in 1984. Nevertheless, it serves as a measure of the cost of living, and illustrates that the penalty has not kept pace with economic values.

Also compared, from 1923 to 1939, and for 1984, is the approximate value of an ox as a function of the penalty. The values for 1923 to 1939 are from Schapera, quoted by Pim (1933). The figure also shows the fines imposed by the Chief's Court, Kanye, in 1929 and 1937. The decline in the value of an ox from 1923 to 1931, was due to drought.

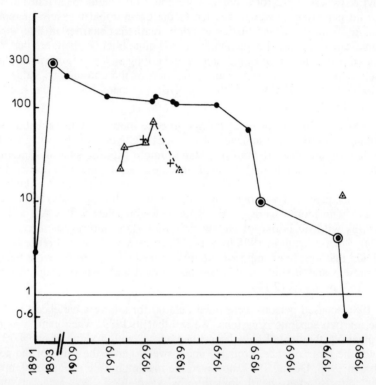

Figure 1. The value of the fine for hunting without a licence 1891–1988.
Blocked circles – the fine as a fraction of the minimum rate of tax. Double circles- penalty revised. Triangles – the fine as a fraction of the value of an ox. Crosses – the value of fines awarded under customary law.

Evolution of the Game Laws

From the relatively simple, but cogent, provisions of the Act of 1886, and the Pro-clamation of 1893, a true *corpus* of game law has evolved. Applied at first only to foreigners, it was inevitable that ultimately the law would come to apply to the whole of the peoples of Botswana. The early pre-occupation of the British Government with game and game laws to the extent that they were one of the considerations of the 1895 settlement, can be seen as resulting from the appalling destruction which had taken place in South Africa in the preceding fifty years: a destruction which threatened the Bechuanaland Protectorate likewise. A massive trade in game products, encouraged by European traders, developed in the latter half of the 19th century, such products comprising the most important exports from the Territory. Schapera (1943) records that one firm alone in Shoshong exported £50,000 worth of products annually at its peak, worth some £1.5 million in today's terms (Pula 4,5 million). But by 1885 the trade had already declined due to drought and over-exploitation, the combined exports from the six stores at Shoshong amounting to an estimated £15,000 per year. The introduction of legislation in 1891 may be seen as designed primarily to curb this trade, and has remained a curb on commercial exploitation to the present day. That such legislation should eventually extend to the population at large was inevitable in view of the increase in population from an estimated 120,776 persons in 1904, to 596,944 in 1971; the adoption of sophisticated methods of game destruction, and the changing patterns of land use leading to reduction in game habitat.

Five major revisions of the principal law have taken place since its introduction: in 1925, 1940, 1961, 1967 and 1979. These revisions introduced little that was new into the basic law of hunting, serving only to make it more detailed. But they did add a number of new concepts relating to the conservation of wild animals in Botswana. Thus, since 1891, we can identify the addition of the following concepts:

- the creation of national parks, game reserves and sanctuaries, whereby species and areas, or species within a defined area, are protected;
- controlled hunting areas, whereby hunting is restricted by area;
- wildlife management areas, whereby the utilisation of game is the principal form of land use in certain areas;
- professional guides, to escort sightseers in game areas;
- professional hunters, to escort sport hunters;
- prohibited methods of hunting;
- Government trophies, whereby the unclaimed parts of dead animals belong to the Government.

The revisions of 1925 were probably influenced by outside opinion, for 1925 was the year in which the first national park was created in Africa (the Albert National Park in the Belgian Congo, now Zaire); while the Kruger National Park in South Africa was created the following year. The 1940 revision was probably in compliance with the 1938 meeting of the parties of the International Convention (London), 1933; but its detail may also be attributed to the fact that offences committed by South African nationals from across the border were often defended by astute lawyers, so that game law had to evolve to counter this. This was unlike other African countries, where offences were usually committed by residents who lacked access to a sophisticated legal body of opinion such as existed in South Africa. Customary law would have been inadequate to meet these changing pressures, and was unenforceable against foreigners, for customary courts could only arraign their own tribesmen. The extensive revisions of 1961, which form the basis of present law, undoubtedly resulted from the formation of the embryo game department in 1959 and the participation of the newly-appointed Game Ranger at the CCTA-IUCN[15] Arusha Conference in 1961, which led to a lengthy debate on new game policy in the newly-created Legislative Council (Appendix IV). It follows that this law would have been revised in 1967 to adapt it to the conditions of Independence; but the opportunity was also taken to tighten a number of weaknesses. The 1979 revision sought to remove the dual application which still existed long after Independence, but at the same time it also liberalised some important restrictive provisions, such as legalising the transfer of licences.

Present law retains, in some form or another, almost all of the original provisions introduced in 1891. Landholder's privileges, for example, were enshrined in Sec. 16 (Act 36 of 1886); and although private game reserves were not formalised until 1961, these have their genesis in Sec. 7 of the 1886 Act. The burden of proof lying with the accused in hunting offences was introduced in 1929 (Proc. 48); but the Act of 1886 placed the burden of proof on the accused to show that the accused was the lawful holder of a licence to hunt (Sec. 14).

Although forfeiture (of guns) was introduced into Cape Dutch law in 1657 *(placaat* of the 1st of January), this did not form a provision of the 1886 Act. The Proclamation of 1904 (Proc. 22) provided for the seizure of property of an accused in lieu of fines, but the provision of forfeiture was not introduced until 1930 (Proc. 27). Sec. 1 of the Proclamation reads: "In the case of a conviction of any person for a contravention of sub-sections (I) and (2) of this section (Sec. 11 of Proc. 17 of 1925) the Court may, in addition to any other penalty imposed, order the confiscation of any firearms and ammunition found in the possession of the accused at the time of the commission of the offence of which he has been convicted ...." This was introduced by Resident Commissioner Rey as necessary to deter poaching. Although originally worded "shall", this was amended to "may" by the High Commissioner on the grounds of there being "some risk of hardship in prescribing that the Court "shall" order the confiscation of the arms whatever might be the circumstances of the case before it" (BNA S.169/6).

In 1952 (Proc. 3) it was extended to include "animal, vehicle or aeroplane"; and in 1961 (Proc. 22) forfeiture was defined as mandatory, including the cancellation of any licence, permit or other authorisation, if the maximum penalty was Rand 200 or more, and related to "any article or thing by means of which or in respect of which the offence has been committed" (Sec. 85) This mandatory forfeiture was extended in 1970 to hunting on private land without permission (Act 64), but repealed in 1979 (Act 1). The operative word remained "may" for offences carrying a maximum penalty of a fine of less than Rand 200[16]. Although it is much disliked, forfeiture is widely used in African game law in both Anglophone and Francophone countries. Rooney (1974) has upheld the South African Courts' interpretation which established that one of the purposes of forfeiture was to enable the convicting Court, by confiscating the articles with which the offence was committed, to inhibit the commission of a further offence. The value of the articles seized was not relevant to the question of forfeitures (State vs. Putter and Putter 1974)[17].

Government trophies were introduced for Crown land in 1940 (Proc. 19), making it illegal to possess the dead parts of any game animal without authority. This Proclamation also introduced the right to search without a warrant for certain authorised persons when an offence was suspected; and also made the hunting of animals at night illegal.

In 1944, HCN No. 25 introduced a permit for the hunting, killing or capturing of large or small game if it was causing damage to property or losses to farming activity in the Tuti Block. This was extended in 1950 (Cap. 114) to "any land", and has now evolved into the allegedly much–abused provision in current law introduced in 1979 (Act. No.1), whereby an animal may be destroyed for "threatening" to cause damage.

28

Proclamation 22 of 1961 made provision for the creation of controlled hunting areas, by which the country could be divided into compartments to allow the setting of hunting quotas by area and give, in theory, better control of the limits to hunting, as was the practice in some other countries. This necessitated that quotas be set for tribal hunting as well. But it was not until after Independence that any controlled hunting areas were declared, beginning with Kweneng District in 1968 (S.I. No. 4), followed by State land in the same year (S.I. No. 15). Following Independence in 1966, the respect originally accorded to each recognised Chief in 1895 concerning management of a tribe's game affairs, was maintained. The Fauna Conservation (Amendment) Act of 1967 (Act No. 47) retained the proviso of Proc. 22 of 1961 that, "except where the context requires otherwise, this Proclamation shall not apply to Africans in tribal territories" (Sec. 4). This resulted in each principal tribe; the Bakgatla, Bakwena, Bamangwato, Bangwaketse and Batawana; having its own hunting Regulations. Each set of Regulations was almost identical, serving to repeat the main provisions of the principal law; but one of their principal effects was that tribesmen now had to pay to hunt. Separate Regulations were promulgated for State land, and for controlled hunting areas on State land. Thus by 1968 there were Regulations for each Tribal Territory (with the exception of the Bakgatla which did not adopt Regulations until 1973), Regulations for hunting in Controlled Hunting Areas in each Tribal Territory (applicable only to persons not resident therein), Regulations for State land, and Regulations for hunting in Controlled Areas on State land (not applicable to residents therein). Six amendments followed up to 1979, when the Fauna Conservation (Unified Hunting) Regulations were introduced (S.I. No. 18), repealing this plethora of regulations and supplanting it with one legislation. But whereas the tribal regulations had been really instruments of acceptance of the main points of the principal law, the Unified Hunting Regulations served mainly to control licensing procedures. The principal law became both *de jure* and *de facto* law throughout Botswana by the deletion of the proviso in Sec. 4 (Act No. 1 of 1979) of Cap. 38:01, exempting Africans in Tribal Territories from the Act's application.

Although it has been argued in some quarters that centralisation of hunting control was a mistake, claiming that it operated better under the tribal administrations because the latter identified themselves with a vested interest in the game, the figures for legal hunting show that, under the former system, over 119,000 licences were being sold each year, with some 33% of the total being killed (40,000 animals) (Tennant 1971). This compares with a citizen quota of 41,373 on offer in 1985, before quotas were reduced because of drought (GN 100 of 1985).

The drawbacks of the universal application of the principal law have been the liberalisation of certain provisions, particularly that of the transfer of licences, and the destruction of animals on the pretext of "threatening" to cause damage. This has been compounded by the decline of penalties as a deterrent, since they have failed to keep pace with economic reality.

Overall, the trend in Botswana' game laws can be seen as leading to:

i. greater restriction on the individual's right to hunt to limit the increased demand.

ii. Tighter control of illegal hunting to anticipate legal dispute.

iii. Limitation on the methods of hunting both for the security of the community at large and to make it less easy to destroy animals in view of the increased demand.

iv. Tighter control of the trade in animal products to provide less incentive for hunting.

v. Tighter control over private landholders, individual property rights being alien to the idea of common ownership of natural resources.

To Whom do Wild Animals Belong?

In 1978 the Attorney General's Chambers delivered the following opinion in reply to a question posed by the Land Development Committee:

"As far as I have been able to ascertain, the Masarwa have always been true nomads, owing no allegiance to any chief or tribe, but have ranged far and wide for a very long time over large areas of the Kalahari in which they have always had unlimited hunting rights, which they enjoy even today despite the Fauna Conservation Act. The right of the Masarwa to hunt is, of course, very important and valuable as hunting is their main source of sustenance ... Without much clearer information it is impossible to give a confirmed opinion about the Masarwa. Tentatively, however, it appears to me that (a) the true nomad Masarwa can have no rights of any kind except rights to hunting ..." (Opinion in Re Common-Law Leases of Tribal Land, 23 Jan 1978).

Without entering into the misconceptions in this statement concerning San social organisation, which have been dealt with by Hitchcock (1978, 1982), it is highly questionable whether statutory law has conferred unlimited hunting rights upon the San. On the contrary, it has denied them hunting rights. Since no Tribal Territory was recognised for the San at the 1895 settlement, as they lacked any articulate representation, one can only interpret the statutory law introduced in 1891, as applying to the San as much as it did to foreigners, unless the San could lay claim to a "Paramount Chief" who could give permission to hunt (Proc. 22 of 1904, Sec. 14). However, those San who accepted vassalage under the principal tribes, in theory had the same hunting rights as the tribesmen. The Resident Magistrate, Ghanzi, wrote to the Government Secretary, Mafeking, on this subject in 1935, pointing out that Bushmen were liable to prosecution under Sec. 30 of the Proclamation as they had no recognised chief (letter of the 5.9.1935, BNA S. 47/9). It was not until 1940 (HCN No. 42) that a proviso was included with relation to the Kgalagadi District that residents of the area could be issued with a permit to hunt and kill game "in reasonable quantities for food"; but this proviso was not repeated again until 1946 (HCN No. 265). And it was not until 1967 that the Fauna Conservation (Amendment) Act (Act. No. 47) included a proviso "Subject to the provisions of any regulation to the contrary regulating the terms and conditions of hunting within a controlled hunting area exempting persons "entirely dependent ... on hunting and gathering veld produce ... where the animal is hunted for the reasonable food requirements of the hunter or of the members of the community to which he belongs ... " from the provisions of the Act, except in respect of conserved animals. The Batawana and Bakwena Tribal Territory Regulations were, however, the only regulations to recognise such hunting (S.I.No. 13 and 37 of 1968). In 1979 the Fauna Conservation Act (Act. No. 1) limited this provision on State land to permitting the Minister to make regulations allowing the "hunting of any animal, other than a conserved animal, in any area by persons resident in that area who are principally dependent for their living on hunting and gathering veld produce, and such regulations may derogate from any of the provisions of this Act. Following this, the Fauna Conservation (Unified Hunting) Regulations, 1979, provided for a Special Game Licence for Remote Area Dwellers, limiting both the species and the numbers which could be taken, but permitting hunting throughout the year.

Thus, far from having unlimited hunting rights, many of the San had less rights until recent years than any other indigenous inhabitant. Although it is commonly stated that the Central Kalahari Game Reserve was gazetted for the San to be able to follow their traditional way of life, the Regulations governing the reserve (GN 38 of 1963) only permit a "Bushman indigenous to the Central Kalahari Game Reserve" to enter the reserve without a permit issued by the District Commissioner, Ghanzi. The establishment of the area as a game reserve (HCN No. 33 of 1961) meant that hunting in the area was forbidden (Sec. 7, Proc. 22 of 1961) except under permit, the conditions of issue of which would not conform to San requirements (Sec. 34). Proclamation 22 of 1961 carried the proviso that the hunting of Royal Game and the law relating to the hunting of animals in general, did not apply to Africans resident on Crown land in respect of hunting on Crown land in the district in which they resided "in accordance with such terms and conditions as may be prescribed"; but this specifically excluded game reserves. The original draft of the Regulations for the reserve allowed for hunting by the San, but this was struck out (see Part II).

According to Silberbauer (1981), among the G/wi San, animals are *kx'o:xudzi* (= to be eaten things), but they are N!adima's creatures (that is, God's), and "as His property they must be respected, not abused. They may be killed in self defence or for food or to avoid an attack that is believed to be imminent". They disapprove of what is seen as greedy hunting, fearing that it will displease N!adima and they will suffer in some way the consequences.[18]

The same people provide us with some insight into how primitive societies evolved control; thus hunting across a border (that is, of a group territory) is not done, but wounded game is pursued into a neighbouring territory. If an animal is brought down only a short distance across the border it is considered to be killed on home ground; but if it flees deep into a neighbouring territory, then the hunter either gets help from that band and gives most of the meat to them, or reports it to them later and gives them the meat (Silberbauer 1981). This is what ancient Roman law said on the subject (Justinian 533 AD): "The question has been raised whether, if a wild animal is so seriously wounded that you can take it, it is supposed to be yours forthwith. Some take this view and hold that it remains yours so long as you continue to pursue it; if you abandon the pursuit, then it ceases to be yours and may be acquired by the first person who takes it. Others maintain that it is not yours until you have caught it. We confirm this view, because many things may occur to prevent your taking it " (Lee 1944).

The G/wi San would therefore seem to practise a compromise of Roman law[19], in that they consider the wounded animal theirs to kill, but yet give much of the meat to the owners of the territory in which it falls. Main (1987) states that the meat and parts of an animal other than the liver and the more perishable portions which are eaten immediately, belong, among the !Kung San, to the person whose arrow was used. Thus they can belong to a person who did not accompany the hunt but simply loaned the arrow which was used to kill the animal. This concept of ownership appears to be unique to the !Kung San[20].

According to my interpretation of Roberts (1969), Kgatla customary law would appear to have similarities to Roman law: "Where more than one person is instrumental in the killing of game, the beast or fowl concerned belongs to the hunter who inflicted the first wound, provided he continues in hot pursuit. The general rule applies even when a wounded animal crawls into someone else's field. Where this takes place, the hunter who inflicted the wound may enter and claim the animal on request to the owner of the field, or his nearest representative".

Ancient British law recognised a common right to game. Thus in the ancient laws of Cambria, written about AD 945: "The stag is said to be one of three common hunts [the other two being bees and salmon]: first, because he is the most gallant and noble animal that is chased with hounds and greyhounds. Secondly, because every person that comes up after he is killed, and before the skin is stripped off, is entitled to a share of him; hence if a person upon his journey come up at that time, he is entitled, by law, to a share as great as the person that killed him" (Probert 1823). It has long been accepted that, after the Norman Conquest (AD 1066), the King assumed ownership of all game (see, for example, Blackstone 1765-9), this assumption perhaps being due to Bracton (circa 1267) who asserted: "by the common Law of this Realm the King has in possession all such things which by the Law of Nature ought to be common, as wild beasts and fowls which are not tame, and which by the Law of Nature may be everyone's who can catch them". Generally, this assumption of a royal prerogative by William the Conqueror is based upon a single reference in the Anglo-Saxon Chronicle (AD 1087): "He set apart a vast deer preserve and imposed laws concerning *it*" (my italics)[21]. Manwood (1598) considered that the authority might be found in the Forest Charter of King Canute (AD1016), article 30 states: "I will, that every free man shall have venison [game] or vert [green trees and shrubs] at pleasure on his own lands, but without chase [the right to punish intruders]; and let all avoid mine, wherever I think proper to have it." Thus Manwood concluded, "By this law it doth appeare, that before that time, all wild beasts were the Kings, wheresoever they were out of the Forest." Canute's Forest Charter is now believed to have been concocted in the 12th century, to justify the Norman forest laws by providing them with an alleged precedent. We shall see that this ancient concept of the King's prerogative has influenced game law to the present day.

In Tswana culture, the ownership of game is not easy to define. On the one hand it was considered to be the property of the Chief, while on the other it was considered that the Chief held it in trust for the Tribe. As a fundamental principle, the Tswana considered all fur-bearing animals as belonging to them, irrespective by whom they were hunted, and their rituals emphasised that they were tribal property (Campbell 1978). Certainly the concept of tribute would seem to imply that game was the property of the Chief, and thus could not be interpreted as *res nullius* – things which belong to nobody but which can become the property of anyone who assumes possession of them through *occupatio*; but rather as *res alicuius*, things being owned (by the Chief). The introduction of a category of Royal Game (Proc.17 of 1925) implied *de jure* ownership by the Crown of certain species outside of the Tribal Territories; but the replacement of this category by the term "Conserved animals" (Act No. 47 of 1967) defines no ownership.

Under ancient Roman law, and we must remember that Justinian's Institutes from which we draw our authority did not refer to a hunting law but to questions of ownership of property; the owner of land was not the owner of the wild animals on such land, which became the property of any person who killed or captured them. Thus wild animals could not be stolen, since they did not belong to any particular person (Greyling 1984). Justinian expressed it as follows:

"Wild animals, birds and fishes, that is all living creatures, which are natives of earth, sea or air, so soon as any one takes them, by the law of nations immediately become his property, for if a thing has no owner natural reason assigns it to the man who takes it. It makes no difference whether wild animals and birds are taken by a man on his own land or on someone else's. Of course, if some one comes upon another man's land for the purpose of hunting or fowling and the owner sees him in time, he may forbid him. Anything you take remain yours so long as you have an effective control over it. When it has escaped from your control and recovered its natural liberty it ceases to be yours and may once again be acquired by the first occupant. An animal is understood to have recovered its natural liberty when you have lost sight of it or when, though within your sight, it is difficult to pursue" (Lee 1944).

Roman law would pose difficulties of application in modern society and the question of ownership has long exercised judicial minds. In the United States, Mr. Justice White, tracing the State's prerogative in legislating for game from the earliest times, averred: "From the earliest traditions the right to reduce animals *ferae naturae* to possession has been the subject of the law-giving power" and referred to French game law as providing an unbroken line of law and precedent from Salic law (circa AD 507-511) summed up by the provisions of the Napoleonic Code (1804), articles 714, 715: "There are things which belong to no one, and the use of which is common to all. Police regulations direct the manner in which they may be enjoyed. The faculty of hunting and fishing is also regulated by special laws." White concluded: "Like recognition of the fundamental principle upon which the property in game rests has led to a similar history and identical results in the common law of ... all the countries of Europe." The learned judge continued: "Undoubtedly this attribute of government to control the taking of animals ferae naturae, which was thus recognised and enforced by the common law of England, was vested in the colonial governments, where not denied by their charters, or in conflict with grants of the royal prerogative" (Geer vs Connecticut (1895) 161 U.S.).

Blackstone, the great English jurist, had rationalised it thus: "and indeed it cannot be denied, that by the law of nature, every man from the prince to the peasant, has an equal right of pursuing, and taking to his own use, all such creatures as are *ferae naturae*, and therefore the property of nobody, but liable to be seized by the first occupant. And so it was held by the imperial [Roman] law. But it follows from the very end and constitution of society, that this natural right, as well as many others belonging to man as an individual, may be restrained by positive laws enacted for reasons of state, or for the supposed benefit of the community ... And in consequence of this authority, we find that the municipal laws of many nations have exerted such power of restraint ... have extended their protection to such particular animals as are usually the objects of pursuit; and have invested the prerogative of hunting and taking such animals in the sovereign of the state only, and such as he shall authorise. Many reasons have concurred for making these constitutions, as ... For preservation of the several species of these animals, which would soon be extirpated by a general liberty ... Nor, certainly, in these prohibitions is there any natural injustice ... since the law does not hereby take from any man his present property, or what was already his own, but barely abridges him of one means of acquiring a future property, that of occupancy, which indeed the law of nature would allow him, but of which the laws of society have in most instances very justly and reasonably deprived him".

Blackstone came to the conclusion that, "if there can, by the law of nature, be any inchoate imperfect property supposed in wild animals before they are taken, it seems most reasonable to fix it in him upon whose land they are found", and this is, with qualification, the present position in English law. It is rationalised by accepting that wild animals cannot be owned, since that would be a contradiction in terms; but as soon as they are reduced into possession, then they become the property of the person on whose land they are when reduced into possession. Thus, in the case of Gott vs Measures (1947), where the defendant shot a dog which was chasing a hare on land over which he had sporting rights, the defendant was ruled against on the grounds that the hare did not belong to him. Had the defendant shot the dog with the hare in its mouth, then the ruling may have been very different; or, if the area had been enclosed so that the hare could not escape and was therefore effectively in the possession of the defendant. du Saussay (1980) states: "Be it called *res nullius* as before or *res communis* as nowadays, practically speaking it is difficult to see why the owner should have a special right over a bird that merely flies over his land". Well, in English law he doesn't, regardless of the fact that the bird may not be taken by other persons.

African legislation differs, in spite of the attempts at uniformity aimed at by international conventions, in its approach to ownership; but is united in the concept that the State controls, and, indeed has ownership, of the game. Some Francophone laws are unequivocal and state "Wildlife belongs to the State", thus removing any ambiguity of interpretation. The State, as custodian of a country, can be seen as having this right of control, and there seems to be no reason why wild animals should be placed in a separate category to the control of other natural resources. Where a country is united as a nation, it is logical, furthermore, that central government assumes the mantle of a Paramount Chief, with a single controlling legislative authority. Botswana presumably bases its State prerogative in this respect on Sec. 86 of the Constitution of Botswana, 1966: "Subject to the provisions of this Constitution, Parliament shall have power to make laws for the peace, order and good government of Botswana". We have seen that Blackstone (see above) would interpret this as including game laws, since such laws can be construed as leading to peace and order, while a lack of them could not be considered as "good government" since this would lead to the squandering of a valuable natural resource. The plaintive cry that God gave wild animals to the people[22] can be seen as a convenient Christian interpretation of Roman law, but the assertion is unrealistic in a modern society where too many people want the same thing. A survey in Botswana (Mordi 1987) suggested that 70.4% of those questioned believed that God and nature would take care of animals; whereas 44.1% believed that wild life was inexhaustible, compared with 46.7% disagreeing and 9.2% having no opinion on the matter. Since it is known that these common beliefs of the inexhaustibility of nature are false, it behoves responsible government to impose wiser council.

It has been argued (Christian 1817), that the sovereign never rightfully possessed any legal prerogative over game in English law. A statute of Henry VII of 1495, for example, states: "... if any person should take any pheasant or partridge upon the freehold of another without the consent of the owner of the ground, he shall forfeit ten pounds ... " (11 Hen VII c17). But it was not until the Game Act, 1831, that the landowner's right of qualified possession was established, following the recommendations of the Game Committee which had been set up in 1816 to study the question of game law revision. The Committee concluded: "It appears that, under the present system, those possessors of land ... feel little or no interest in the preservation of the Game; and that they are less active in repressing the baneful practice of poaching, than if they remained entitled to kill and enjoy the Game found upon their own lands. Nor is it unnatural to suppose, that the injury done to the crops, in those situations where Game is superabundant, may induce the possessors of land, thus circumstanced, rather to encourage than to suppress illegal methods of destroying it."

"Resolved – That it is the opinion of the Committee that all Game should be the property of the person on whose lands such Game should be found" (quoted in Christian 1817). This concept now finds difficulty of acceptance in Africa, since it tends to contradict the statutory law as originally introduced by colonial administrations, which the indigenous peoples saw as taking away what they considered as their right of possession, even although this did not apply in the Tribal Territories of Botswana.

Roman, Dutch, or English Law?

The origin of statutory game law in South Africa is found in a series of instructions issued to counter the rapid disappearance of wild animals at the Cape. This situation was provoked, to a large extent, as it was in later years, by commercialisation; one cause being the re-victualling of ships with meat. The instructions, or *placaaten,* were not impositions of Dutch law in the sense that Aguda (1973) quotes the repeal in 1959 of Sec. 6 of the *placaat* of the 4th of October 1540 relating to marriage, where a section of Dutch law had been simply transposed to Cape law (and from thence to Botswana law). The game *placaaten* were, on the contrary, *de novo* in origin. Thus the first of these, forbidding the shooting of birds, was introduced by the Governor Van Riebeeck on the 1st of January 1657, within five years of his settlement there (Rabie 1973). This was followed by other *placaaten* in the same year, and in 1667, 1668, 1680, 1687, 1751, 1771 and 1792. In 1680 Governor Simon van der Stel introduced the first comprehensive criminal prohibition of unlawful hunting, with a licensing system, a hunting season limited to two months of the year, and the condition that a part of any lawfully hunted carcase of a hippopotamus must be left for the wild animals. We can identify the introduction of the following provisions in the *placaaten:*

- forfeiture of gun 1.1.1657;
- fine 1.1.1657;
- recidivism 3.10.1667;
- licence to hunt 8.4.1680;
- hunting season 8.4.1680;
- corporal punishment for recidivism 8.4.1680;
- taking of eggs from nest prohibited 27.4.1751;
- disturbance of game prohibited 27.4.1751;
- establishment of "game protectors" 27.4.1751;
- power of arrest for game protectors 27.4.1751;
- control of dogs in protected areas 3.9.1771;
- game protectors empowered to shoot uncontrolled dogs 3.9.1771,
- game protectors empowered to search carriages and huts and confiscate guns 3.9.1771;
- "Governor's licence" for protected areas 18.9.1792;
- sale of game shot without licence forbidden 18.9.1792.

To quote Rabie (1973):

"They [the Cape Governors] all asserted that they would stop and eradicate illegal hunting ... Fines for the contravention of the placaats were doubled, corporal punishment ... was retained, and forfeiture of any rifle found in the possession of the accused was decreed. Sale and purchase of unlawfully obtained game was prohibited and anyone going into the veld accompanied by a dog, had to provide the dog with a heavy cudgel, tied around its neck, in order to prevent it from catching any game[23]. The concept of hunting was widened and also included the disturbance and capture of game".

Although all of the *placaaten* were *ultra vibes*, they were, nevertheless, *de facto* law (Bothma and Rabie 1983). After the British took control of the Cape in 1815, the Roman-Dutch civil law which operated was left largely intact, while inequalities under the criminal law were removed by specific legislative action (Wilson and Thompson 1982). The essentially Roman-Dutch law thus became the common law of Botswana in 1891 (Thompson 1959), although Brewer (1974) argues that the Roman-Dutch law had been considerably influenced by then by English law and that the term "Cape colonial law" would be more appropriate; but this does not indicate the strong element of Roman law which was retained. In the transposed Game Law Amendment Act, 1886, half of the provisions identified above as occurring in the *placaaten* were dropped; forfeiture, corporal punishment, control of dogs, game protectors and their powers, and the Governor's licence. The reintroduction of all of these at a later date into Botswana law (with the exception of corporal punishment), was undoubtedly in ignorance of their previous use in Cape law, their introduction arising *de novo* for the same reasons as they had arisen in old Cape law.

Aguda (1973) has argued that the Cape law introduced in 1891 was "in the eyes of modern jurists, primitive", and was not subsequently developed by professional judges. But the same criticism in the sense of the law remaining a *jus antiquum* does not apply in respect of the game law, which was constantly being evolved by the Administration, although not in response to judicial interpretation. Since 1964 there have been only eight reviews quoted in the Botswana Law Reports, and these have not led to changes in the law, although some of the interpretations have been significant (e.g. State vs Mosinyi and Others 1972, concerning *mens rea*; and State vs Masedi 1980, concerning assisting another to hunt). But it has not suffered the stagnation of inappropriate received law that Brewer (1974) and Molokomme (1985) identify, for example, in other areas of the laws of Botswana.

The Fauna Conservation Proclamation, 1961, appears to have been structured upon Ordinance 43 of 1954 of Northern Rhodesia, which in turn was influenced by the Game Ordinance, 1937, of Kenya (cap. 216), following the recommendation of Pitman (1934). This latter law (whose antecedent was Ordinance 58 of 1921), was probably as much influenced by early South African law as was the first Botswana law, through the medium of the Convention of 1900. But Proclamation 19 of 1940, was already a detailed piece of legislation of 30 sections. Incorporating some of the sections of Ordinance 43 brought the total number to 95, as against only 49 in Ordinance 43. Therefore, although the Botswana legislation was influenced by this Ordinance, it was by no means a copy of it, on the contrary, it tended to be much more complex and verbose, even where sections were adopted. There were, for example, 39 definitions in the Botswana law, compared to only 16 in the Northern Rhodesian legislation. An example of how the law increased in complexity is given by Sec. 45. This section appears to have had its genesis in this form in Sec. 26, cap. 216 Kenya, 1937, as follows:

– "No person shall hunt, kill or capture a game animal on private land without the consent of the owner or his agent or the lawful occupier of such land."

The previous Ordinance (1921) was worded in a rather different manner (Sec. 23(1)):

– "Any Resident may take out a Private Land Licence which will entitle him to hunt, kill or capture game on private land only with the consent of the owner or occupier, and the holder of such licence may by payment of the difference in amount of the licence fees convert it into a Resident's Full Licence."

In Ord. 43 of 1954, Sec. 15 (1) (Northern Rhodesia), Section 26 above becomes:

– "No person other than the owner or occupier shall hunt or be found in circumstances showing that it is his intention to hunt on private land without the authority of the owner or occupier of such land previously sought and obtained, and for the purposes of this subsection the carrying of fire-arms on private land shall be *prima facie* evidence of intention to hunt."

Sub-section (2) continues:

– "Except as provided by section thirty-eight of this Ordinance, nothing in this Ordinance shall be construed as granting authority to any person to enter upon the land of another, save in pursuit of an animal lawfully wounded by such person outside the boundaries of such land and then subject to his making a report of the circumstances with all reasonable despatch to the occupier thereof."

In the Fauna Conservation Proclamation, 1961, it becomes (Sec. 45 (1)):

– "No person shall enter upon any land for the purpose of hunting or capturing any animal without the written permission of the owner or occupier of such land or unless he is accompanied by such owner or occupier or the duly appointed representative of such owner or occupier."

Sub-section (2) then provides penalties for the offence, and the section continues with sub-section (3):

–"If a person is seen or found on any land in possession of any firearm or other weapon capable of killing any animal by the discharge of any missile, or any poisoned bait, poisoned weapon, bird-lime, net, gin, trap or snare, or with a dog, he shall be deemed to have entered upon such land in contravention of the provisions of this section, unless he proves

   (a) that he had the permission of the owner or occupier of such land ...; or
   (b) that he was not upon such land for that purpose".

This is followed by a further sub-section (4):

– "Any policeman or the owner or occupier of any land who finds any person mentioned in sub-section (3) of this section upon such land may require such person to satisfy him that such person has permission to enter upon such land as required under sub-section (1) of this section and, if such person is unable so to satisfy such policeman, owner or occupier, may demand from such person his full name and address and may direct him forthwith to quit such land, and if such person fails to give his name and address or gives a false or incomplete name and address or fails forthwith to quit such land after being directed so to do, he shall be guilty of an offence and liable to the penalties prescribed in sub-section (2) of this section."

English game law viewed this as primarily trespass, or unwarrantable entry onto another's land; whereas the above law places the stress upon the taking of the game rather than upon the entry onto the land.

To take another illustration of the increasing complexity introduced into borrowed law, the destruction of dogs appears in the Kenya Ordinance 58 of 1921 (Sec. 8) as follows:

– "Any Game Warden may destroy any dog found at large and not under control within a Game Reserve."

Sec. 23 (7) of cap. 216, 1937 (Kenya) reads:

– "Any dog found at large and not under control within a game reserve may be destroyed by order of the administrative officer in charge of such area or of the Game Warden."

In Ordinance 43 of 1954 (Northern Rhodesia) this becomes (Sec. 5 (3)):

– "Any dog found at large and not under control within a game reserve may be destroyed by or by the order of an authorised officer or any Administrative Officer."

And in the Fauna Conservation Proclamation, 1961, it becomes (Sec. 88 (2)):

– "It shall be lawful for any game officer to destroy any dog found hunting any animal on land other than private land, if such dog is not in the keeping of or accompanied by a person who is lawfully upon such land."

The equivalent in English game law would appear to be that of a legal "park", which is a fenced area in which are kept beasts of chase, whose owner may shoot a dog chasing game in it (Wright vs Ramscot, 1 Saund. 84, n. 3). But otherwise, as we have seen, it is not permissible to shoot a dog hunting game (Gott vs Measures 1947). Under Roman law, domestic animals were expected to behave decently (Lee 1944) and the owner was generally liable for any bad behaviour, but the law was only specific on the question of keeping dogs near a public road, which was disallowed.

The section on the registration of ivory and rhinoceros horn is almost identically worded in Ord. 43 of 1954 (Northern Rhodesia) (Sec. 33 (1)) with Proc. 22 of 1961 (Sec. 69 (1)); but again the latter is more verbose. This, however, relates to implementation of the International Convention, 1933, (see below), so that one would expect to find similar, if not identical, wording in all African law.

Particular provisions taken from the Northern Rhodesia Ordinance and introduced into Botswana law were:

– the creation of licensing officers and honorary game officers (Sec. 2, Sec. 43 of Ord. 43);
– the category of Private Game Reserves (Sec. 6 of Ord. 43);
– Controlled Hunting Areas (Sec. 8 of Ord. 43);
– restriction of licences to bird, general [ordinary] and supplementary (Sec. 12 of Ord. 43);
– the obligatory maintenance of a register of species taken (Sec. 19 of Ord. 43);
– a professional guide (hunter) required a licence to operate (Sec. 13 of Ord. 43)
– a trophy dealer's licence was required (Sec. 30 of Ord. 43).

Rather than being completely alien, these provisions may be seen as improvements to existing law, generally regulating existing situations. For example, the genesis of Private Game Reserves is found in the very earliest Botswana statutory law (Sec. 7 of the 1886 Game Law Amendment Act). Defining them as Private Game Reserves brought greater regularity to the concept, but whereas Ord. 43 (Northern Rhodesia) empowered the Director to declare such reserves, in Botswana this could only be done by the Resident Commissioner. Botswana law was therefore stricter, and such borrowed law was not introduced without tailoring it to what was seen as Botswana's needs. There was certain to be an interchange of concepts between African countries, since this was an objective of the international conventions. The underlying precepts, however, tend to be facultative, and not imitative of other, extraneous legal systems. The complexity introduced into Botswana's borrowed law tends to forestall case law; for whereas a simple clause may leave the interpretation of its meaning open to debate, the inclusion of all foreseeable alternatives tends to eliminate this possibility.

Botswana's judges normally resort to South African decisions as to authority in game cases (e.g. State vs Mosinyi and Others, quoting R vs van der Lind, 1953 (1), S.A. 588), since English game law is generally inappropriate, although it has played some part in influencing Botswana game law. The very word "game" is taken from English law[24], first used in 1389 (13 Rich II c.13); but certainly there was no transposing of sections of English game law into the Act of 1886, nor into the Proclamation of 1893, although the following principles of English game law are included, namely:

- the observance of close or fence seasons, first introduced into English game law for the protection of deer in the breeding season in 1225 (9 Hen III); and for game birds in 1609 (7 Jac I cl 1);
- a person must have the landowner's permission to hunt on private land, first referred to in English law in 1495 (11 Hen II c17);
- a moiety of any fine imposed to be paid to the person whose information led to the conviction, first referred to in English game law in 1706 (5 Ann c14), but which was, apparently, an ancient practice dating from at least Elizabethan times (18 Eliz c5, 1576);
- possession of a licence to hunt, first introduced into English game law for the purpose of raising revenue in 1784 (24 Geo III c43), but only certain persons were allowed to hunt and the purchase of a licence did not alter this.

The Plumage Birds Protection and Preservation Proclamation of 1914, and the subsequent Wild Birds Protection and Preservation Proclamation of 1933, while from their titles appearing to be based upon the Wild Birds Protection Acts of 1880 and 1896, do not, in fact, bear any resemblance to the latter English Acts. For whereas the English Acts were for the protection of wild birds during the breeding season, the Botswana Proclamations were for the prevention of trade in wild birds.

When the Protectorate Administration first imposed statutory game law with the 1893 Proclamation, English game law had been liberalised by the 1831 Game Amendment Act. This Act established the qualified right of the landowner to the game on his land and did away with the qualification statutes, by which a person had to possess a certain amount of property and income before he could hunt. Apart from this, the law maintained close seasons and a prohibition on killing game on Sundays and Christmas Day; provided for the sale of game by licensed dealers; prohibited the purchase of game from non-licensed dealers; prohibited trespassing in search of game; maintained protection of royal forests and gave the right to any lawful game owner to seize unlawfully obtained game. Hunting at night was an offence under the Night Poaching Acts of 1828 and 1844.

The term Royal Game, introduced into Botswana law in 1925 (Proc.17), is not found as such in English law. Although some Norman kings laid title to all game until the Forest Charter of 1215 limited their prerogative (the alleged laws of Canute of 1016 referred to deer as "Royal beasts"), the only animals designated specifically as "Royal" were, and are, swans, whales and the sturgeon. The term was never applied to other animals as a class; but a "hart royal" for example, under the ancient forest laws, was a deer hunted by the sovereign which had escaped and was granted protection from further hunting (Manwood 1598)[25]. Prior to the Game

Amendment Act, 1831, the royal prerogative referred to areas rather than to species, the forest laws only referring to animals within the royal forests.

From the beginning of this century, game law in Africa has occupied a unique position in legislative procedure, in that it has derived from a number of international conferences. Thus it does not reflect any one particular country's law, e.g. English game law, but rather an amalgam of European attitudes; although one in which the early foundation laid by South African game law undoubtedly played an important influencing role. The first such conference was held in 1900, and attended by Britain, France, Germany, Spain, Italy, Portugal and Belgium (the Congo Free State). After considering the existing African legislation, and also that of India and Burma, and after inviting comments from such persons as Selous[26]; the countries signed a Convention for the Preservation of Animals, Birds and Fish in Africa, which, although never ratified, formed the basis of the 1933 International Convention, the Convention Relative to the Preservation of Fauna and Flora in the Natural State, which was so, taking effect from January 1936. This second conference was attended by Britain, France, Belgium, Spain, Italy, Portugal, Egypt, the Anglo-Egyptian Sudan and South Africa; with the High Commission Territories of southern Africa represented jointly by the High Commissioner. Its Convention made provision for the creation of national parks and other protected areas by contracting governments (Art.2,4,7); protected species (Art. 8); and encouraged "the domestication of wild animals susceptible to economic utilisation" (Art. 7 (2)). It introduced the regulation of both internal and import/export traffic in, and manufacture of, articles made from trophies (Art. 9 (1)), and required the possession of an export certificate for exported items (Art. 9 (2)). Ivory and rhinoceros horn had to be marked and the weight recorded (Art. 9 (5)); while "found ivory, rhinoceros horn and all trophies of animals found dead, or accidentally killed, or killed in defence of any person" were to be government trophies (Art. 9 (6)). Prohibited methods of hunting were agreed; namely the use of motor vehicles or aircraft for hunting, killing or capturing; or for driving, stampeding or otherwise disturbing game. Landowners or occupiers could, however, use such methods if they were not otherwise illegal (Art. 10 (1)). Other prohibited methods of hunting were:

– fire-ringing;
– the use of poison or explosives for killing fish;
– the use of dazzling lights, flares, poison or poisoned weapons;
– the use of nets, pits or enclosures, gins, traps or snares, set guns or missiles containing explosives (Art. 10 (2)).

The Parties reviewed the Convention in 1938, but proposed amendments were not confirmed, although this led to the introduction of extensive legislation in Botswana in 1940, when the majority of the above provisions became law (Proc. 19 of 1940).

In 1953 it was reviewed again at Bukavu, although this was a technical conference without competence to adopt a final decision. Among the conference's recommendations were the creation of a new category of protected animals, class 'C', which consisted of species threatened with extinction in a part of their range; and the drafting of a new convention, which was completed in 1964. In 1967, a revised convention, the African Convention on the Conservation and Management of Wildlife, was drawn up with inputs from 32 African countries, but superseded by the former which became the Organisation of African Unity's African Convention on the Conservation of Nature and Natural Resources, 1968; ratified by 28 out of the 50 signatories.

These conventions served to introduce standard formats and concepts into African game law, based upon international consensus originating first in European thought, and from 1964 resulting from an African consensus. Such law is much more detailed than, for example, English game law; which although addressing protection, is more preoccupied with concepts of property ownership and the rights of the individual, rather than the State control of a resource.

The Fauna Conservation Proclamation of 1961 reflects the majority of the recommendations of these conventions, but several concepts of English game law are discernible, apart from those identified above in the first Botswana game laws. Foremost among these are:

– hunting at night, forbidden under English law since 1485 (1 Hen VII c.7), the original objective being not so much one of preserving the game, but of ensuring that armed persons were not abroad at night on the pretext of hunting, as the preamble indicates: "... Forasmuch as before this time divers ordinances and statutes have been made in divers parliaments holden in the same realm, for the punition of inordinate and unlawful huntings in forests, parks and in warrens within the said realm, which statutes and ordinances notwithstanding, divers persons in great number, some with painted faces, some with visors, and otherwise disguised, to the intent they should not be known, riotously, and in manner of war arrayed, have oftentimes of late hunted, as well as by night as by day ... if any person or persons hereafter be convicted of any such huntings, with painted faces, visors, or otherwise disguised, to the intent they should not be known, or of unlawful hunting in time of night, that then the same person or persons so convict to have like punition, as he or they should have, if he or they were convict of a felony."[27]

– Prohibition on the buying or selling of game legally hunted. Occurring first in English game law in 1540 (32 Hen VIII c. 8) when the buying or selling of pheasant or partridge was forbidden. The sale of game was not legalised until the Game Amendment Act of 1831.

– The searching of dwelling houses by authorised persons with a warrant was introduced into English game law in 1670 (22 and 23 Car II c25): "the said gamekeeper or gamekeepers, or any other person being thereunto authorised, by a warrant of a justice of the peace, may, in the day-time search the houses..." Burn (1785) has commented as follows: "It is at least safe to have such a warrant, especially if any houses are to be entered and searched. For it would give too great a power to the gamekeepers to leave it in their discretion to search what places they may think proper, as also to constitute them the judges, whether a person is or is not qualified [under the English law] to kill game. Therefore it is best to have a warrant from a justice of the peace..."

– Assisting another to hunt was decided by the Courts as permissible if the person did not actually hunt himself. Thus Chitty (1812) stated: "It appears to have been long established that the penalties imposed by the game laws, do not attach upon one who, not being qualified, attends and assists one who is so ..." Thus in the case of the Queen vs Green (1712), Chief Justice Parker commented: "That such persons ought to be taken as servants of the qualified party ... it cannot authorise a person to shoot at game in company with one who is qualified ..." And in the King vs Newman (1771) Lord Mansfield stated: "Shall not a gentleman take any body out with him to beat the bushes, and see a hare killed?"

41

– The confiscation of arms by authorised persons dates to 1776 (16 Geo III c. 30): "That if any person armed shall enter any forest or other place, where deer are usually kept, whether enclosed or not, with intent to take deer, the ranger or keeper may seize and take from such person, for the use of the owner of the forest ... all guns and other engines, and dogs there brought for coursing deer ..."

There is some resemblance between the wording of Sec. 31 of the Game Amendment Act, 1831, and Sec. 45 (4) of the Fauna Conservation Proclamation, 1961 (Sec. 47 in cap. 38:01); but there is no transposing of sections as such.[28]

It could be disputed that the above examples are basic concepts which would arise independently in any game law, without reference to other sources. But let us remember that the colonial legal draughtsman, asked to prepare game law legislation, in all probability would consult English game law to determine the principles upon which it is based. This would have been a constructive approach, because English game law was directed at the culmination of a process which in Botswana was at its beginning; that is, preserving game in the face of high human population pressures, and in a situation where the majority of the land was in private ownership. English game law has been remarkably successful in this, for since the Forest Charter of 1215, only one game species, the bustard, has become extinct in England, and that in the latter part of the 19th century. An exception to this was wolves and boars, but this was because people were encouraged to destroy them. Other species of animal also became extinct, but were not legislated for as game. If Botswana loses no more than one of its game species in the next six hundred years, then it could be justly proud of its game laws!

Thus Botswana game laws may be said to have traceable Cape Dutch and English influences, but these have been diluted by an oecumenism of thought contributed by many countries, so that today the law reflects a cohesion of approach to establishing rules designed to both protect and exploit a natural resource, in keeping with the increased demands placed upon it by man's increasing independence of, and subjugation of, nature.

Conclusion

From time immemorial some conception of restriction upon the taking of numbers of wild animals has existed; whether in the San belief of angering N!adima, or in the Tswana Chief exercising control through organised hunts. The Tswana have been exposed to game laws, other than their customary law tribal restrictions, from the middle of the 19th century; and we cannot be sure that they were not familiar with the Cape *placaaten* before then, even although they would not have been applied to the Tswana. But such customary laws and beliefs as were operative, were inadequate in the face of the commercial rewards offered by European traders in the 19th century for skins, feathers and ivory. The San themselves sold skins to traders, although forbidden to do so by the Tswana chiefs in their areas. Since the creation of the Protectorate there was a progressive increase in the scope and complexity of the customary laws in imitation of those statutory laws applied by the Administration. This was entirely voluntary, as the Administration would have no powers to coerce the Chiefs to protect species; and we have seen that the precise instructions of the Colonial Office were, in fact, never followed nor insisted upon.

Statements such as that of Mordi (1987), "... the laws were parachuted, fully-formed into the society. They were literally imposed by the government on a people apparently unaccustomed to perceiving animals in capacities other than meat", have no basis in fact. The same author quotes Kallen (1964) as stating that, in primitive societies, "an innovation must be assimilated by the ways of the fathers before it can be accepted", and, "innovations must be received through the vehicle of tribal culture". Aguda (1973) has argued that the laws, in a general sense, have been imposed upon the country *ab extra,* implying that they are not relevant to the people's needs: "law grows with the people it is meant to serve and should be in a large measure a reflection of their spirit and mores". But such concepts are not new, and to quote Hailey (1953): "It became the recognised official practice to encourage the Chiefs to make use of their traditional power to make laws, rather than to legislate by enactment, and a number of instances could be quoted in which the Chiefs were urged to use this procedure in order to effect purposes in which the Administration was interested. Thus they were on several occasions urged to make their own laws for the protection of big game in their areas".

In 1934 the Administration issued a Proclamation (Proc. 74) empowering it to issue orders through the Chiefs; a Proclamation which was met with some resistance.[12] As Hailey (1953) explains: "The effect of the measures then enacted was prejudiced by a technical error – the failure to appreciate that in building up a system of local rule on a foundation of indigenous institutions it is expedient that as little change as possible should be made in their traditional form. All experience shows that so long as the form is respected, there is always a possibility of making such subsequent changes as experience of the practical working of the institution shows to be desirable. The extent of these changes will depend on the measure of popular acquiescence they secure, but the indigenous institution may, given this measure of acquiescence, be completely modified in the course of its adaptation to modern purposes without incurring a resistance which would make its working difficult or infructuous".

We can trace a considerable caution in the introduction of game laws in the manner in which areas were protected from hunting for periods of no longer than one year at a time, necessitating, in the case of the Ghanzi and Kgalagadi Districts, renewal of the Notice twenty-one times before the period was increased to three years, and the legislation finally dropped in 1961. Thus statutory laws were not thrust upon the people "fully formed". Statutory laws applying principally to foreigners, in the tribal areas customary law continued in force until nine years after Independence. It was not until 1967, seventy-two years after the first introduction of statutory law to the country, that customary law was replaced by the Tribal Hunting Regulations, which were, in effect, brief summaries of the principal law. This could be seen, perhaps, as part of the trend towards the abolition of customary law in favour of written law (see, for example, Brewer (1974) on the criminal law of Botswana). It was not until 1979 that the Unified Hunting Regulations came into being and the principal law finally became of universal application. The Unified Hunting Regulations related mainly to licensing procedures and did not summarise the principal law as the tribal regulations had done. Adoption of the principal law was thus a very slow, stepwise process, such that by the time that it became universal it was already well-known and accepted through the medium of the local authorities, providing indeed a classic example of the manner in which new law should be integrated. There was nothing abrupt in its reception, neither did it diverge widely from that which was commonly accepted, even if not whole-heartedly endorsed. If influences can be traced in it of Cape Dutch law, then as

Pain (1978) has argued, "In richness of general principle and wealth and diversity of sources, the Romano-Dutch legal system has no peer", so that this is no cause for rejection. We can see this richness in the 1886 Game Law Amendment Act, with its far-sighted provisions for domestication and scientific investigation; provisions almost a century ahead of their time. As to English game law, there was no transposing of sections, even although influences may be detected which were adapted to give the Botswana law more substance. In his carefully balanced study of African customary law, Elias (1956) writes: "It [African law] is thus no longer to be set in opposition to what is frequently but loosely termed 'European law', and this notwithstanding a number of admitted differences of content and method", and " ... British Colonial Africa ... may also have to face sooner or later the same types of problem which beset the path of legal evolution everywhere". While Elias was defending the status of African customary law, his conclusions implied that, in view of the fact that it formed "part and parcel of law in general", it was justified to merge it or replace it with European-type statutory law, since there was no irreconcilable division between the two systems.

Why were game laws made? If such a question needs to be asked, the answer must be that they were made out of a concern by the Administration for the future well-being of the country. If game laws had not been introduced, then the fauna of Botswana would undoubtedly have suffered the same fate as did that of South Africa; and today the former Protectorate Administration would be vilified for having allowed this to happen, to the loss and detriment of Botswana in general. That this did not happen should be cause for approbation rather than denigration.

Dawson, in his quaint way, summed up the reason for imposing game laws as long ago as 1694 (Dawson 1694):

"We are therefore farther to consider, that these wild beasts having so many deserts and vast coverts to live quietly in, would quickly multiply into great numbers, and would then become very troublesome both to tillers of the ground, and to keepers of sheep, and other tame cattle, being some of them such, as would eat up their corn, and the grass which their cattle should eat; and others such as would devour the very cattle themselves ... From whence two things are evident: First, that where there is but a few people, the wild beasts will be sure to multiply. And secondly, that lest they should do so, it was lawful for all men to kill and destroy them. And indeed there is no doubt to be made, but that for a long time the *Ferae naturae,* viz. all beasts by nature wild, belonged to all those who could take and kill them ... So that as long as men in any place were not multiplied to such a number, as with ease might keep the wild beasts so much under, as that they should not be able to hurt them, it is not to be imagined any laws would be made for their preservation; and therefore that for so long time there were no such forests [that is, royal forests where hunting was forbidden] as were afterwards. We are therefore farther to consider, that in the process of time, as men did multiply there would in every nation be still less and less waste ground and woods, and thickets, which might be for dens and coverts of wild beasts; and by consequence, that their numbers also would be greatly lessened, seeing they had not where to hide themselves, and to lie and be quiet, and breed as before. And seeing, moreover everyone was an enemy to them, and would still go on to kill them, as in former times; some, because they found the flesh of them to be delicate food, and to yield a most excellent nourishment; others, because they fed upon that which their tame cattle were to feed on, or devoured the very tame cattle themselves; and some, because they found it an exercise both delightful and healthful to hunt them down, or otherways to kill them ... And so when this was come to be the state of affairs, viz. that men were much multiplied, and that wild beasts were all like to be destroyed; seeing all could not eat of such delicate and strengthening food as venison, nor all have the use of the noble exercise of hunting ... And thus, I say, at last, were Laws made for the preservation of wild beasts, those woods and thickets and waste places in which they had covert, and Officers appointed to see those laws executed".

It could be argued, in contemporary vein, that Britain's early pre-occupation with game preservation, to the extent of including conditions in the 1895 settlement, was in order to restore the once important trade in game products, and so derive an economic benefit for herself from the Protectorate. Parsons (1969) has shown how such trade once played an important role in the economic life of the Tswana, was instrumental in shifting power from the Bakwena to the Bamangwato, and caused the expansion of the Ngwato State; but by 1885 overhunting and drought had caused the collapse of the trade. Nothing in the documents of the time suggests that economic benefit was Britain's motive, whose actions were engendered solely by a genuine concern to halt the slaughter; a concern which was already Africa-wide at the beginning of the century. That this concern had such a powerful voice, able to influence decisions of the Colonial Secretary, was due to the influential personages involved. Thus when the Society for the Preservation of the Wild Fauna of the Empire was launched in 1903, it had, as Vice-Presidents: Lords Cromer, Grey, Milner, Curzon of Kerdlestone and Minto; all leading figures of the day. The Secretary of State for the Colonies was himself an honorary member. The disastrous effects of the rinderpest epidemic in 1897 added to the concern, leading to the convening of the London Covention in 1900. Events in Botswana were thus only a part of a much wider initiative, but nevertheless maintained a unique independence of approach.

Von Richter and Butynski have expressed the result thus (1973): "As in many other countries free roaming wildlife is not the property of an individual but is held in trust by the State for the people and future generations. The State will promulgate laws and regulations which will allow people or groups of people to hunt and utilise wildlife, but it must ensure that this is not done at the expense of others. In Botswana wildlife is considered as a national asset which must be used for the national benefit".

The law relating to fauna conservation in Botswana remains essentially a "game" law, unlike some countries not having progressed to include plant life, while fish are excluded from the definition of "animal". As du Saussay writes (1984): "Obviously, if one considers the object pursued by these two Conventions [i.e. the African Convention of 1968 and the Washington or CITES Convention of 1973] and also, be it noted, by the London Convention [1933], it is natural to ask why the law governing wild fauna and that governing the flora should be distinct, and whether they should remain so; and, again, whether they should be brought together at least as regards their presiding principles in a body of law catering for living entities of nature (or, if the expression is preferred, for living renewable natural resources). Such a body of law, moreover, would simply be a domain of the law of natural resources or, in more general terms, of the environment and nature protection. The fundamental identity of the problems arising in the conservation of the fauna and flora and the ecological interdependencies linking the one to the other argue for a single law comprehending both".

It is clear that the evolution of Botswana's game laws has yet further to progress, both in the all-embracing concept of "wild life", and to remove the lingering dichotomy of approach as exemplified by having an independent Act for national parks, implying that game on State land is of universal ownership, but not that on Tribal land; to conform to international law such as the Convention on Trade in Endangered Species (CITES or the Washington Convention, 1973); and to facilitate the wise utilisation of game as a renewable natural resource. It is the latter consideration that du Saussay (1984) sees as perhaps the principal refinement that will take place in African wild life law in the future: " ... the improvements that it is desirable to incorporate into positive law should be geared in the first place to developing the resource or, to put it in other terms to augment a capital that can be made to yield returns and, secondly, to securing a fairer distribution of the benefits to be expected from this source". Such a development is to be welcomed if it does not return us to the situation prevailing in Botswana in the late 19th century.

But commercialisation can only be a success if a right to property in game is recognised, whereas Botswana law subordinates ownership to State control. This approach fails to appreciate that what a person does not own, he has no commitment to nurture if he visualises the benefit as accruing to others. Nevertheless, whatever else may be said against the Protectorate's game laws, they did at least impede, if not halt, the large-scale, commercially motivated destruction of Botswana's game, permitting today's generation to enjoy some of the former richness of spectacle. Botswana can consider herself fortunate that the proposed policy of game destruction outside of protected areas mooted in 1961 (Appendix IV), was never put into practice, but was replaced by the more enlightened views contained in the Wildlife Conservation Policy of 1986, promulgating the principle of wise use of the resource.

Notes to Part I

1. This was first referred to in English law in 1604 (2 Jac I c27) "An act for the better execution of the intent and meaning of former statutes made against shooting in guns, and for the preservation of the game of pheasants and partridges, and against the destroying of hares with harepipes, and tracing hares in the snow", which, in its preamble states: "... whereby the good thereby meant and hoped hath not succeeded, and thereby great scarcity of the said games in all, or in the most parts of this realm, hath followed, and presently is, and so is like to be, if some remedy be not in that behalf provided".

2. From May 1977 Kenya imposed a total ban on hunting.

3. Compare the law in Italy and Portugal, where an owner may not oppose the entry of hunters onto his land, although there are limitations concerning enclosed properties or land which may be damaged, e.g. growing crops.

4. The system of land tenure in Botswana would seem to be similar to that which formerly held elsewhere in Africa, see, for example, Meek (1946), Elias (1956); while we can detect its underlying rationale in Maine, who wrote, without any knowledge of Tswana custom: "It is in the peculiarities of an undeveloped society that we see the first traces of universal succession. Contrasted with the organisation of a modern state, the commonwealths of primitive times may be fairly described as consisting of a number of little despotic governments, each perfectly distinct from the rest, each absolutely controlled by the prerogative of a single monarch. But although the Patriarch ... had rights thus extensive, it is impossible to doubt that he lay under an equal amplitude of obligations. If he governed the family, it was for its behoof. If he was lord of its possessions, he held them as a trustee for his children and kindred. He had no privilege or position distinct from that conferred on him by his relation to the petty common-wealth which he governed ... He enjoyed rights and stood under duties, but the rights and the duties, were, in the contemplation of his fellow-citizens and in the eye of the law, quite as much those of the collective body as his own". (Maine 1861).

5. See Camphell (1980) for a description of the different hunts.

6. This was a widespread tradition in Africa, but it is unlikely to antedate the 16th century Portuguese commerce in ivory. In Benin (Nigeria) any hunter, other than the king's, was required to hand over to the king a leg and the *largest* tusk of every elephant killed (Egharevba 1946).

7. Namely the prohibition of hunting on Sundays. This had been prohibited in England since 1773 (13 Geo III c80) but the reason was probably not religious. Since a labourer was obliged to work for the rest of week, and hunting at night was prohibited, this effectively prevented him from hunting at all.

8. See Parsons (1969).

9. Legislation was first introduced by Proclamations of the High Commissioner. After the creation of a Legislative Council in 1960, its enactments were known as Laws, and after a Parliament was instituted in 1966, they became Acts.

10. Tlou (1985) interprets this as a curtailment of the traditional rights of the African rulers, and this view was probably accepted by the Administration for the provision was repealed in 1904 by Proc. 22. The Chiefs then apparently set their own fee, which was equal to the Administration's licence fee. This practice was continued until the Tribal Hunting Regulations came into force in 1967. However, although written permission was subsequently required for a foreigner to hunt in a Tribal Territory, provided he had a licence to hunt issued by the Administration, it would appear that he could hunt with impunity in a Tribal Territory, since customary law applied only to the tribesmen in their own Territory, and a foreigner could not be arraigned under customary law.

11. Amended by Proc. 1 of 1911 to the 1st day of October.

12. See Hailey (1953) pp 218ff, for a discussion of this controversial proclamation, which was modified by Proclamation 32 of 1943.

13. See the Rey diaries (Parsons & Crowder 1988). Rey records that while on tour on the 20.2.1931, Hottentots living 16 miles from Tshane requested permission to shoot game for food. Rey gave permission to shoot wildebeest, gemsbok and springbok only for a six months' trial period; after which the permission would be cancelled if it was found that they were exporting biltong. He noted that the Hukuntsi people were "delighted" with the permission to shoot game for food. This suggests that the law was fairly well obeyed.

14. Other tribes replaced the term "Tribal Authority" with the word "Chief".

15. Commission for Technical Co-operation in Africa South of the Sahara and the International Union for the Conservation of Nature. "The Symposium on the Conservation of Nature and Natural Resources in Modern African States" was "to inform and influence public opinion through its leaders and responsible persons in the Governments, that the application of conservation practices based on ecological knowledge, is in the best interests of all African countries..."

16 English law interprets "may" as "shall" in this context, and on this basis the Courts have consistently mis-interpreted the provision. For example, Judicial Circular RM22 of the 9.9.1976 states that subsection (1) of Section 89 of the Fauna Conservation Act cap. 38:01, gives magistrates a discretion. This is also implied in the appeal judgement De Graaf vs The State (Cr. Appeal No. 118 of 1985); and in Mpinyane vs The State (Cr. Appeal No. 6 of 1986). But there is a number of precedents to the effect that enabling words are construed as

compulsory whenever the object of the power is to effect a legal right. This principle was decided in the famous case of Julius vs The Bishop of Oxford (1880) (5 A.C. 214), where the point is discussed at length as to whether "may" meant "shall". To quote Lord Blackburn in the case: "I should say, for instance, that if, by enabling words, a Court is empowered to pass sentence on one convicted of a crime, it would be the duty of the Court to pass that sentence". Thus "may" has the meaning of "shall", being directory, and the Magistrate must therefore order forfeiture where the word "may" is not qualified to allow discretion.

17 Under English law, guns and other weapons may be confiscated by the Court whether or not those particular guns and other weapons were actually used in the commission of the offence upon which the Court has convicted, or in poaching the game found on the defendants (Game Laws (Amendment) Act 1960, Sec. 3 (iii)). Botswana law is much more liberal, in that only guns or other weapons which can be proved to have been actually used in the commission of the offence, may be forfeited (De Graaf vs The State, Cr. Appeal No.118 of 1985).

18 Early law has often resulted from the codification of religious beliefs.

19 It is not the intention to imply that Roman law somehow found its way into early southern Africa societies; the object is to determine whether disparate societies arrive at the same conclusions.

20 Compare the ancient Indian laws of Manu, *circa* 200 BC-200 AD,
"Sages who know the past declare ... a deer [to belong] to him who owned the arrow which first struck it".

21 This was the New Forest, where the punishment was blinding for killing a deer, and later, castration also. Although it was also forbidden to hunt other game there, it is not clear whether this bore the same penalty, although it is generally assumed so. Rackham (1986) gives a different translation to that of Garmonsway: "The king [William] set up great protection for deer and legislated to that intent, that whosoever should slay hart or hind should be blinded..."

22 In the 19th century "poaching wars" in England, the poachers claimed that they had a God-given right to take game: "... they say God has made the game of the land free and left it free" commented one Justice of the Peace (Munsche 1981).

23 This was perhaps preferable to the mediaeval English Forest Law practice of "lawing" dogs to prevent them hunting: "And such lawing shall be done by the assize commonly used, that is to say, that three claws of the fore foot shall be cut off by the skin". (9 Hen III, 1215).

24 Now being replaced by the American term "wildlife", defined by Partridge (1969) as "Gobbledeygook for all wild creatures – and even for wild plants."

25 The prerogative of the English crown to declare royal game, which was maintained under the Forest Charter of 1215, was not abrogated until 1971, when the Forest Charter was fully repealed; only swans, whales and the sturgeon remaining as royal game (Wild Creatures and Forest Laws Act, 1971).

26 Frederick Courtenay Selous, D.S.O., 1851-1917. Hunted in Botswana *circa* 1875 to 1889, was one of the leading naturalist-big game hunters of his time.

27 Hunting at night has come to have a very different relevance, for animals are more easily taken then if blinded by lights.

28 Sec. 31 of the Game Law Amendment Act, 1831, reads as follows: " ... where

any person shall be found on any land ... in search or pursuit of game ..., it shall be lawful for any person having the right of killing the game upon such land ... or for the occupier of the land ..., to require the person so found forthwith to quit the land whereon he shall be so found, and also to tell his christian name, surname, and place of abode ... "

Compare Sec. 4 (4) of the Fauna Conservation Proclamation, 1961: "Any policeman or the owner or occupier of any land who finds any person ... upon such land ... may demand from such person his full name and address and may direct him forthwith to quit such land ..."

Part II
History and Evolution of the Protected Area System[1]

Introduction

Although Botswana was one of the few African countries which did not have a national park until after Independence, traditional Chief's hunting preserves apart, its history of statutorily protected areas goes back much earlier than 1967. As provided for in Sec. ll of the 1886 Game Amendment Act, Proclamation 17 of 1925 included enabling legislation for the High Commissioner to protect Large and Small Game in any prescribed area for a period not exceeding three years (Sec. 5). The London Convention of 1900 had made specific provision for the establishment of game reserves (Art. II,Sec. 5): "Establishment, as far as it is possible, of reserves within which it shall be unlawful to hunt, capture or kill any bird or other wild animal except those which shall be specially exempted from protection by the local authorities.

"By the term 'reserves' are to be understood sufficiently large tracts of land which have all the qualifications necessary as regards food, water, and, if possible, salt, for preserving birds or other wild animals, and for affording them the necessary quiet during the breeding time".

But since this convention was never ratified, its provisions were not applied, and the legislation in the Protectorate continued to be based upon the Cape law (although South Africa had already declared four game reserves by 1898). It was not until 1938 that the Protectorate began to prepare legislation enabling game reserves and sanctuaries to be established, undoubtedly in response to the London Convention of 1933 and its 1938 conference. The London Convention defined a national park[2] , and a strict natural reserve (Art. 2 (1), (2)); and contracting governments were required to "explore" the possibilities of establishing such areas within two years of the date of the conference, or select suitable areas as early as possible (Art. 3). Settlement should be controlled in national parks, while controlled hunting zones should be established around them. The areas should cover, as far as possible, any migratory routes (Art. 4). There was also provision for reserves, where there should be no hunting except for scientific or administrative purposes, or the protection of life and property (Art. 7 (1)). Contracting governments were also obliged to "encourage the domestication of wild animals susceptible to economic utilisation" (Art. 7 (2)).

Enabling legislation for game reserves was enacted in Botswana in 1940 (Proc. 19). This was followed in the same year by the declaration of a game reserve along the Nossop River (HCN No. 107 of 1925).

The Arusha Conference of 1961,[3] which, as we have seen, was attended by Botswana's Game Officer, undoubtedly influenced the creation of the Chobe Game Reserve, and focussed Botswana's attention on the game resource. At the First Session of Botswana's newly-created Legislative Council, the Administrative Secretary opened a lengthy debate on Botswana's game policy by referring to the Arusha Conference and continuing:

"I quote this because it is evidence of the very great interest in the preservation of wild life which is now to be found in Africa and which we all agree is to be very warmly supported. It is evident that the preservation of wild life has an economic value of its own, and in all our proposals it must never be thought that we are suggesting that all our wild life should be exterminated. Very far from it. We would like to give far more attention to our wild life, to concentrate our efforts in various places and turn them into an even greater asset than they are now. We would all agree that the wild animals of the Bechuanaland Protectorate are amongst its greatest glories and none of us would willingly wish to see the game stamped out. We would all like to see it preserved where it can be preserved without detriment to other interests and turned into an asset which people could come and enjoy and which would also bring revenue to this country.

"Many will ask, why should we reverse our policy of game preservation, where elsewhere in Africa people are awakening to the tragedy of having shot out their wild life, and are now beginning to make strenuous steps to counter this? But I would remind honourable Members that the Bechuanaland Protectorate is not in the same position as other territories. There the reduction of wild life has gone very far indeed and it is therefore a cause of particular anxiety. Here in most parts of the Protectorate it has not gone anything like as far as that, and this Government has already, in any case, established two very large Game Reserves whose area is vast and compares favourably with anything established in any country in Africa. Whatever our Game Policy may be in future those Game Reserves must be developed and must be sacrosanct and they will, I repeat, bear comparison so far as their natural wealth is concerned with any country in Africa. So in that respect we have nothing whatever to be ashamed of.

"As you know there is every intention of developing the Chobe Game Reserve. We have been handicapped by lack of funds in the past, but we have hopes of funds being made available in the next few months, which will enable us to make a start with developing game tracks etc. in the Chobe Game Reserve to develop it as an asset. So we hope that the Chobe Game Reserve will be developed as a major tourist industry, making its own contribution to the economy and life of this country.

"Therefore there is no reason why Bechuanaland should not continue to be as good an example as any in Africa in this regard. Indeed as I say, even if wild life were only to be protected in Game Reserves, the Bechuanaland record would be unsurpassed by any Central African or Southern African Territory". (Douglas 26.10.1961).

Consequent upon Independence in 1966 it was possible to promulgate a National Parks Act, enabling Government to accord the internationally accepted level of state protection on areas, as well as on the animals within them[4]. The National Parks Act, 1967, came into force on the 8th of March 1968; although under this Act national parks have little difference in legal standing from game reserves created under the Fauna Conservation Act. Whereas the former are established by an Order of the President published in the Gazette (cap. 38:03, Sec. 3); the latter require a Notice (cap. 38:01, Sec. 6). Thus, the only difference with regard to legal standing is that whereas an Order is directory in meaning, implying some action to be taken, a Notice is simply informative; although no great weight is placed on the difference between the two terms. The fundamental difference is that game reserves and sanctuaries created under the Fauna Conservation Act only protect the animals within them, and not the land or habitat, although the Minister may make regulations to protect the habitat as well (Sec. 99 (2) (c)). Further, national parks can only be created on State land, or on land "bequeathed or donated" to the President, or to another, for the purpose of a national park; and gazettement is subject to appeal. On the other hand, game reserves or sanctuaries may be declared by the President on any area of land, and there is no provision for appeal against the gazettement. Hence national parks have only been created on State land, and game reserves have been reserved for Tribal land. But the law has seemingly been used also to provide game reserves as a stage in the creation of a national park (compare the Chobe Game Reserve and its Regulations). The maintenance of this dualism of application of the game laws concerning State land and Tribal land (see Part I), means that, in Botswana today, there are three national Parks on State land, and three major game reserves. While there are only two major game reserves on Tribal, now District, land, and no national parks. Campbell (1973) provides an outline description of these areas.

Traditional Protected Areas

Little information survives on traditional protected areas, but these were usually in the form of Chiefs' hunting preserves akin to the Royal Forests of England created by William the Conqueror in the 11th century[5]. Such a reserve was Chief's Island in the Okavango Delta, known formerly as "Mathuiba's Island" after the Tawana Chief who set it up sometime after 1906. Khama, Chief of the Ngwato, had a "reserve" for ostriches in 1875 in the region of Makwa, some way south of Sua Pan (Tabler 1960). This may have been the same private reserve which Tshekedi Khama had somewhere between Serowe and Rakops sometime between 1925 and 1949. It was stated in 1941 that he had a game reserve northwest of Serowe in which he did not allow hunting by his tribe (BNA S.15/2). Under Khama (1875-1923), sometime after 1902 Serowe Hill was created a sanctuary for hyrax and guinea-fowl. Generally speaking, however, there was little need for protected areas before the era of exploitation which began in the middle of the 19th century, and the Chiefs hunted with their people in the common hunting grounds. Thus the present Khutse Game Reserve lies in a Kwena traditional winter hunting area, but it was not reserved in any way. Khama's "ostrich reserve" was set up as an area to allow ostriches to breed in undisturbed, because of the great decline in numbers which had taken place and the scarcity of feathers for trade.

No-hunting Areas

In view of the lack of enabling legislation to protect areas, the first statutorily "protected areas" were no-hunting areas; areas on Crown land where, initially, the hunting of large game was forbidden, and later, small game as well. Although the legislation at first made no distinction, it was primarily aimed at foreign hunters and some recognition of indigenous rights usually prevailed. The first application of this legislation (Sec.1 of Proc. 2 of 1907) was in 1924, when all Large Game was protected for a period of one year on all Crown land "north of the Molopo River" (HCN No. 20 of 1924). This could be construed as throughout Botswana, although that was not the intent of the legislation which, after being repeated the following year, in 1926 was amended by the addition of the words "northwards to the 24th parallel" (HCN No. 18 of 1926), thus covering an area of about 88,000km[2]. This legislation was prompted by complaints from the South African National Parks' Board of Trustees, which alleged that game was being shot out on the Botswana side, and that coloured families settled on the Botswana side of the Nossop River, poached in the Gordonia Game Reserve. The latter was an area of 18,600km[2] re-proclaimed as a game reserve in South Africa in 1923. In 1925 there were reports of dead game lying "strewn over the veld" in this area. The complaints from South Africa continued in spite of the legislation, legislation which the Resident Commissioner did not appear to be aware of, as in 1928 he informed the South African National Parks' Board of Trustees that legislation was being drafted to restrict hunting on the Botswana side (BNA S.166/1). In that year (1928) the annual Notice lapsed, and new legislation appeared in 1929 expanding the scope of the previous Notice to include land extending northwards between the border with Namibia and longitude 21° E to latitude 22° 30'S, thus encompassing an area of some 105,000km[2]. In 1930, the Kalahari Game Reserve (4,720km[2]) was declared in South Africa (Cape Province Proc. 68 of 1930), replacing the Gordonia Game Reserve, which was de-proclaimed.

In Botswana the Notice was repeated annually until 1940, when it was expanded to cover the "whole of the Kgalagadi District", thus in effect adding another 15,750km[2] to the area protected (HCN No. 42 of 1940). The annual Notice continued until 1950, after which it became triennial until it lapsed in 1961.

In 1929, Large Game was protected for a period of one year on unalienated land in the Tuli Block, an area of some 2,500km[2] which had been sold to European farmers[6]; but this was not repeated (HCN No. 23 of 1929). In 1932, protection of all Large and Small Game for a period of three years was announced in an area of 24,000km[2] in the Chobe District (given as 15,550km[2]) with a view to declaring a game reserve (HCN No. 53 of 1932). The following year the area was increased to 31,600km[2] (given as 20,740km[2]), and the Notice then repeated triennially until 1943, when it was allowed to lapse. In 1938, all large and small game birds were protected for a period of three years within a radius of 6kms (9.4km[2]) of Mogobane

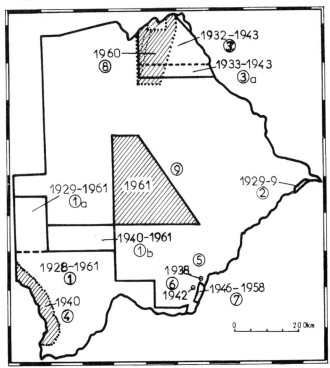

Map 1. No-hunting areas, sanctuaries and game reserves, 1926-1961.
(1). (la), (lb), no-hunting area; (2) no-hunting area; (3), (3a), no-hunting area; (4) game reserve formely included in (1); (5) no-hunting area, declared a sanctuary in 1940; (6) sanctuary; (7) no-hunting area; (8) game reserve; (9) game reserve.

Dam in the Bamalete Reserve (HCN No. 44 of 1938). In 1946, all Crown lands in the Lobatse District (600km²) were closed to hunting for one year (HCN No. 193 of 1946), and this continued until 1958.

Map 1 and Figure 2 (page 68) show the changes in the total area in which game was protected from hunting between 1926 and 1961, when the last of these Notices lapsed. From Rey's diary (Parsons and Crowder 1988) it would appear that there was at least some observance of these restrictions (see Part I, note 13).

Game Reserves

The annual Notices protecting game on the Botswana side did little to alleviate the complaints from South Africa's National Parks' Board of Trustees concerning alleged poaching in the Kalahari Gemsbok National Park, which requested that the coloured families living along the Nossop River in Botswana be removed. Rey, who had been appointed Resident Commissioner in 1930, instituted an inquiry in 1933 as a result of which he declined to take action since the people claimed that the accusations were false; adding that they could get all the game that they wanted on the Botswana side. They were, in fact, issued with licences permitting a limited amount of hunting, as we have seen, despite the annual Notice. It was contemplated that, rather than remove the people, a police post would be opened at Tsabong when funds became available. But subsequently the South African police caught a number of poachers *in flagrante delicto* and by 1937 Rey had supported the removal, but only if the people themselves agreed to move and they were paid compensation. This was conveyed to the Board of Trustees, and it was intimated that a game reserve would be created on the Botswana side. As a result, the South African "Star" newspaper of the 4th of March 1937, carried an item headed "The Imperial Government's Gift of Land", stating that an area on the Botswana side was to be ceded to South Africa to form a part of the Kalahari Gemsbok National Park (BNA S. 108/2/1)[7]. Rey hastened to disabuse the South Africans of this idea, but before any further moves could take place he was succeeded by a new Resident Commissioner, Arden-Clarke. The latter fully endorsed Rey's ideas, for by May of 1938 the people, totalling 280 persons from five locations[8], had all been removed (some to Bokspits, while others returned to South Africa from whence they had come in 1913). The cost of removal and compensation was borne by the South African National Parks' Board of Trustees (BNA 5.108/2/2).

In the following year the Resident Commissioner informed the Board of Trustees that legislation was being prepared which would permit the gazetting of game reserves "in different parts of the country" (BNA S.108/2/3). As we have seen, the enabling legislation came with Proclamation 19 of 1940 (Sec. 5). This was immediately followed by the creation of the game reserve along the Nossop River (HCN No. 107 of 1940) on the 25th of June, totalling some 9,700km² (given as 6,040km²). Even this did not stop the complaints from South Africa and, after repeated representations, the warden of the Kalahari Gemsbok National Park, J.D. LeRiche, was appointed honorary Game Ranger for Botswana's game reserve; this being possible under the new legislation (Sec. 28 of Proc. 19 of 1940) (BNA 5.108/2/3)[9]. This resulted in a further news item, this time in the "Rand Daily Mail" of the 12th of September 1940, to the effect that the reserve had been given to the Board of Trustees[10]. Due to the intervention of the War, nothing further could be done at this time, and LeRiche was given permission to demarcate the southern boundary of the Reserve. A dispute with the displaced families who had settled south of the Reserve almost immediately ensued, for the new boundary was put in the wrong place; due to imprecise instructions being given to LeRiche, and to the fact that he did not take into account magnetic variation when tracing his line by compass bearing. Eventually the boundary, was re-located in its correct position. Complaints of poaching still continued from South Africa, and in 1962 Botswana's Director of Veterinary Services minuted that the Reserve was a liability and best handed over to South Africa. He stated that it could not be guaranteed that it would not be de-gazetted at some future date (BNA S. 213/7/1).

Events leading to the creation of the Chobe Game Reserve were more purposeful, and seemingly had their origin in a tour of several eastern and central African countries by Major R.W.G. Hingston in May 1930, who was commissioned by the Society for the Preservation of the Fauna of the Empire to recommend areas for the setting aside as national parks. Hingston did not include Botswana in his itinerary, and this led to Rey angrily noting that once again Bechuanaland had been ignored. Not to be outdone, Rey called for suggestions for a suitable area for a national park to be established in Botswana. How much he may have been also influenced in this by a colleague in South Africa we cannot tell, but a letter from J.G.Gubbins, dated 1931 and therefore sometime after Hingston's tour, read:

"... I cannot help thinking that the thing which would always carry your name down the river of fame would be the establishment of the foundations of a great game reserve ... The sightseer of the future will come by aeroplane so accessibility is nothing".

Rey replied (7.9.1931):

"My dear Gubbins ... I agree with you as to the creation of a game reserve and I am going to take the matter up; whether I shall be succesful or not, I cannot say as yet, as I have not been into it sufficiently, but anyhow I am going to try"[11]. (BNAS. 238/14).

In his diary (9.9.1931 to 15.9.1931) Rey wrote: "The idea is to protect all the wonderful game in Ngamiland from extinction, and to attract visitors to see them. Thousands of people go to the Victoria Falls every year. If we can put up a good hotel at Kasane and protect the game, the visitors will come on into Ngamiland, spend money, and open up and develop the Territory. It's a great scheme, and I think can be done without our having to spend money. There's wonderful fishing there too and altogether I don't see why it shouldn't be one of Africa's show places". (Parsons and Crowder 1988).

The first site proposal Rey received was from the Acting Resident Magistrate for Maun, V.F. Ellenberger, who suggested a small area of about 3,500km[2] between the eastern boundary of the Tawana Reserve and the 'new' motor road to Kasane (Map 2). A larger area, comprising most of the Chobe Crown lands, appears to have been suggested by the Acting Resident Magistrate for Kasane, Captain Beeching. This area, Rey confirmed, fulfilled almost all of the nine requirements for a national park suggested by Hingston (Hingston 1930)[12].

In a memorandum of the 8.3.1932, Rey wrote: "I have in view not merely the preservation of the fauna of the Protectorate (which might otherwise undoubtedly become extinct at no distant date) but also to assist in the development of the Territory, financially and otherwise". He emphasised the importance to tourism of the proximity of the Victoria Falls, and proposed a hotel at Kazungula. Hot springs between Kasane and Kazungula were also seen as an attraction which might rival Harrogate. He pointed out the economic advantages of tourism as shown by the rapidly growing popularity of the Kruger National Park in South Africa (created in 1926[13]), and Zimbabwe's Hwange National Park (established as a Game Reserve in

1928 and declared a National Park in 1930). Rey also stressed the need for the idea to be developed gradually, dropping his earlier enthusiasm for a national park and proposing that it be first a game reserve, then later a national park. Perhaps he had begun to meet with opposition to the idea, but there is only one objection on file which followed his first step, that of prohibiting hunting in the area (HCN No. 53 of 1932). This objection came from Chief Konkwena of Munga[14], who sent a letter to the Officer Commanding, Kasane, on the 21st May 1932, as follows (translation):

"Morena, I your servant say that we have heard your law of guns and we are sad. We are respectfully requesting you to speak on our behalf to the Government that the country had become hard and bad. We your people have been accustomed to carry guns wherever one wishes to go, we will not be able to walk with only hands. Your people say that they are sorry and I myself am sorry in a different way. Then we all look in to you for you are one with a sharp knife and we are your servants, this is what your people said because their sadness is great that guns should be left in huts. Lions this time in winter and we shall be finished, we shall be killed by lions. This is what your people wanted me to speak to you. Awaiting your reply.

Yours obediently
S.E. Konkwena."

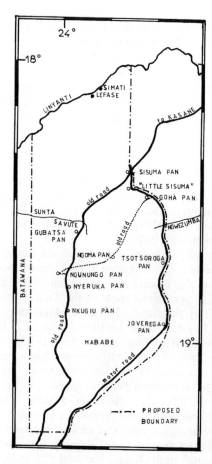

Map 2. First proposal for the Chobe Game Reserve, 1931 (with original spellings).

During a tour by Rey in the north in 1933, at a kgotla held in Maun on the 17.6.1933, the Tawana requested permission to trap game in the Reserve, which was refused (Parsons and Crowder 1988). Later objection came from the Government Veterinary Officer, H.H.Webb, who minuted that he had been opposed to the reserve from the start, considering that it would encourage the spread of tsetse fly and sleeping sickness (Minute of the 11.3.1935), (BNA S.238/16) .

After prohibiting hunting, Rey's next step was to propose asking the Society for the Preservation of the Fauna of the Empire for funds to build roads in the area; but a reply from the Colonial Secretary, Sir. E. Harding (8.6.1932), suggested that he refrain from doing this until a decision had been reached on East Africa, following Hingston's recommendations for that region. Rey could not do other than acquiesce, but nevertheless, in June 1933, he proposed that Captain Beeching act as unpaid Game Warden for the area, in addition to his duties as Resident Magistrate, until such time as funds were available for a Game Warden to be appointed (BNA S. 238/15).

The area was officially closed to hunting until 1943, after which year no more Notices were issued. This was due to the eastwards spread of the tsetse fly and an increase in the incidence of sleeping-sickness in the Maun area, which resulted in definite plans being instituted for tsetse control in 1943 (Davies n.d.). For the moment, this put an end to Rey's dream (Map 3).

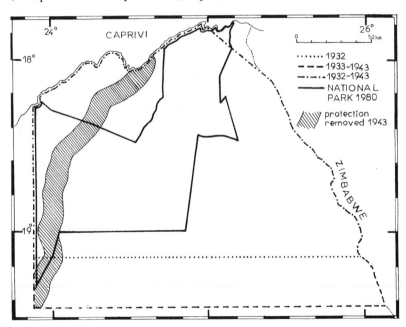

Map 3. The Chobe no-hunting area 1932-1943, with the present area of the Chobe National Park.

On the 1st December 1956 a Game Control Unit was formed, ostensibly to control elephants on private land in the Tuli Block. But the enthusiasm of the Game Ranger, Major P. Bromfield, did not limit itself to elephant control, and by 1957 he had already reconnoitred several areas with a view to creating a game reserve in the north. An area in the Chobe District was considered to be the most suitable for this purpose and had official sanction from the Divisional Commissioner, (North). In a letter of the 28.8.1957, he apologised for "overlooking the matter" and proposed a northern game reserve of about 21,000km² reaching from the Tawana border in the west, in a southeast direction to link up with Zimbabwe's Hwange National Park. The Divisional Commissioner noted that the area:

a) would preserve the east-west migratory routes in and out of the Hwange National Park, and

b) it was useless for other purposes due to the presence of the poisonous plant *mogau (Dichapetalun cymosum)* and the lack of arable land.

Two possible extensions were also proposed: one of some 2,800km² to include the Ngwezumba-Nogotsaa area; and another of some 2,700km², if the Colonial Development Corporation vacated it, to join this area to the Zimbabwe border, and hence the Hwange National Park (Map. 4) (BNA S. 568/13/1).

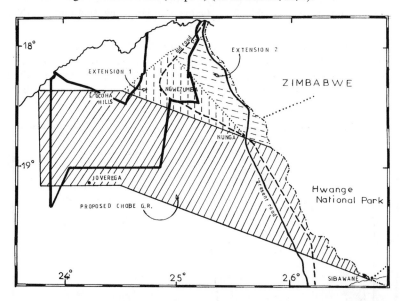

Map 4. Chobe Game Reserve proposal, 1957.

The matter was pursued by the Game Ranger in 1958–9, and debated by a committee on the 5th August 1959 which recommended the Reserve's establishment. As a result, the Chobe Game Reserve, reduced to an area of 15,400km², was gazetted on the 14.7.1960 (HCN No. 65 of 1960); but leaving a corridor in the east to allow for the movement of cattle to Kazungula, and thus severing the connection with the Hwange National Park. On the other hand, the area was provided with access to the Chobe River, which had not been included in the original plan.

On the 27.9.1961, the newly-formed Legislative Council voted Rand 26,000 for the Reserve's development; but its establishment was not without opposition. In a minute prepared for the Legislative Council's debate of the 26.10.1961, in which the establishment of the Reserve was upheld (see Introduction), the Director of Veterinary Services stated that he had been opposed to the idea from the start [again!] and continued: "... our cattle industry can never be put onto a proper footing if we are going to consider the game" (minute dated the 16.9.1961) (BNA

S. 584/3). The Senior District Officer (Development) minuted (11.9.1961): "... this Territory, in its present financial position, cannot afford the luxury of a Game Department that cannot balance its budget, or nearly so. This I think it could easily do if it confined its activities to the management of the Chobe Game Reserve and the controlled hunting of safaris ..." (BNA S. 584/3).

The tsetse fly was still a problem, but it had not prevented the Reserve from being gazetted.

In 1964, the boundaries were altered, reducing the area to 10,800km^2 by mainly excising the portion south of latitude 19°S (which has never been put to any other use since than hunting), and an area in the northwest along the Linyanti River (Map 5).

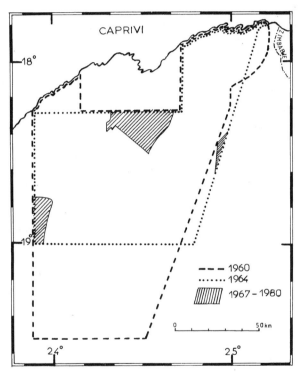

Map 5. Chobe Game Reserve, 1960–1980.

Following the gazettement of the Chobe Game Reserve came the declaration of the largest game reserve in Africa (now the third largest), the Central Kalahari (Kgalagadi) Game Reserve totaling an estimated 52,800km^2, which was gazetted on the 14.2.1961 (HCN No. 33 of 1961) (Map 1). With the creation of this game reserve, the protection Notices for the Kgalagadi District and the area in the west of Ghanzi District, ceased. The establishment of the Reserve resulted from the recommendations of a survey of the San, although the report was not issued until 1965 (Silberbauer 1965). It was proposed that an extensive area of Crown land be set aside to enable the San to follow their traditional hunting and gathering way of life, but it was considered that the establishment of a tribal reserve for this purpose would meet with opposition from the Ghanzi European farmers to the west, and probably also from the Ngwato to the east; these groups fearing that they might lose their labour supply if the San chose to inhabit the reserve. The alternative was to create a game reserve, giving the San full hunting and occupation rights within it. The Game Reserve was, as had been supposed, established without opposition. The Bushman Survey Officer, G. Silberbauer, then drafted regulations giving any San who was resident in the area for more than four months of the year, the right to hunt *all* species of game throughout the year, and to keep smallstock in the Reserve.

The first item that was struck out from Silberbauer's draft regulations was that relating to hunting, with the observation that this was entirely contrary to the enabling legislation. This interpretation is open to question, as permission to hunt could have been given under Sec. 34 (b) of the Fauna Proclamation, 1961, as a form of utilisation. It was implied that the question would have to be settled locally, presumably meaning that the authorities could turn a blind eye to hunting if they wished. The next item to be deleted was the provision permitting the keeping of smallstock; so that when the Regulations finally appeared (GN No. 38 of 1963), the only concession granted to the San was that they could enter the Reserve without first obtaining a permit in writing from the District Commissioner, Ghanzi (Reg. 2). Thus the hunting activities of the San in this area became illegal (see Part I), and Silberbauer could only protest that this was entirely contrary to the assurances that he had been given. His protest was filed with a red interrogatory mark against it[15].

In 1976, the boundaries of the Bakwena Tribal Territory were revised under the Tribal Territories Act, 1976, following a proposal originally made in 1966; and the southeast corner of the Central Kgalagadi Game Reserve, comprising an area of 1,036km[2], was included as a part of the Bakwena Tribal Territory and *de facto* excised from the Game Reserve, although legislation was never promulgated to this effect as is required under Sec. 6 (c) of the Fauna Conservation Act. Thus the *de facto* area of the Central Kgalagadi Game Reserve is now approximately 51, 800km[2].

A "Fact Finding Mission" mounted by Government in 1985, which examined the status of the Reserve with respect to the San settlements which had developed there (a "blind eye" having indeed been turned to the activities of the San following gazettement of the Reserve), recommended that the area south of latitude 22°S, covering some 34,000km[2], be de-gazetted and proclaimed a Wildlife Management Area, leaving some 17,100km[2] as game reserve (Pilane *et al.* 1985). This followed earlier proposals that the area north of latitude 22°S should become a National Park, and the remainder a Wildlife Management Area (Sherburne et al 1974, von Richter 1976). The proposal of the Fact Finding Mission was rejected by Government, which ruled that the boundaries "should be maintained as at present" (Matsetse 1986), and the residents encouraged to move out to areas where better services could be provided for them. A report in support of a resolution to the European Parliament, stated that the adoption of a proposal to divide the area into two would be contrary to the European Communities Commission recommendations and the wishes of the European Parliament (Galland 1986).

Hitherto, game reserves had only been declared on Crown land, but in 1964 the first game reserve on Tribal land was announced; the Tawana having been encouraged to gazette their own reserve, the Moremi Wildlife Reserve[16], an area of some 2,000km[2] between the Khwai and Mogogelo rivers in Ngamiland. This reserve was administered by a society formed for that purpose, the Fauna Preservation Society of Ngamiland, as provided for in its Regulations (GN No. 137 of 1964), and formally established in 1965 (LN No. 14 of 1965).

In 1976, the boundaries were extended eastwards to connect with the southwest corner of the Chobe National Park, and westwards to include the traditional protected area of Chief's Island, enlarging the area to 3,900km^2 (SI No. 93 of 1976). Finally, in 1979, the Reserve was handed over to central government to be run by the Department of Wildlife and National Parks, becoming the Moremi Game Reserve with a new set of Regulations (SI No. 102 of 1979).

A little-known reserve, the Nuane Dam Game Reserve, covering an area of 1.05km^2, including the water surface, was created in 1969 in the Lobatse District (SI No. 122 of 1969). This was simply a measure to prevent the hunting of animals coming to drink at the dam.

Following a request by the Department of Wildlife and National Parks for a study for a game reserve in the Boteti River-Nxai Pan area, a report by an American Fulbright Scholar, D. Birkenholz, recommended that the Boteti River area be made a "management area" which could include hunting (Birkenholz 1967). This was established as the Makgadikgadi Pans Game Reserve in 1970, covering an area of some 4,130km^2 (SI No. 83 of 1970). This was followed in 1971 by two more Game Reserves; the Mabuasehube Game Reserve of 1,665km^2 adjacent to the Gemsbok National Park an important pan area; and the 2,600km^2 Khutse Game Reserve adjoining the southwest border of the Central Kgalagadi Game Reserve, (SI No. 10 of 1971 and SI No. 78 of 1971 respectively). The latter area was chosen to secure an ecologically important pan area against cattle encroachment and to provide a Kalahari Desert experience within easy reach of the capital, Gaborone, since the Central Kgalagadi Game Reserve was closed to visitors (Parris, pers. comm.). Initially the Bakwena were encouraged to establish it as their own Tribal Game Reserve, but it was eventually gazetted under central government control.

In 1974, the 700km^2 Maikaelelo Game Reserve was declared (SI No. 145 of 1974), but de-gazetted in 1980 (SI No. 125 of 1980). This was followed by the declaration of the Gaborone Game Reserve of some 3km^2 in 1980 (SI No. 138 of 1980), and in 1985 by the 3km^2 Mannyelanong Game Reserve in the South East District (SI No. 89 of 1985). The latter was designed to protect a nesting site of the Cape Vulture, and had been proposed for protection in 1976 (von Richter 1976). The area appears to have first been mentioned by Bryden (1893) who wrote: "Prominent among the mountains of this district, between Boulder Pits and Ramoutsa, is Aasvogel Kop[17], a headland celebrated from time immemorial as the resting-place of vultures, and noticeable at great distances in the surrounding country".

Sanctuaries

Sanctuaries were first provided for in the 1940 Proclamation (Proc. 19), and are designed to protect specified species within an area without curtailing the uses of the area. The first application was to the Mogobane Dam in the Bamalete Reserve, where certain birds had been protected under HCN No. 44 of 1938. After consultation with the Chief, the area within a radius of 6kms of the dam (9.4km^2) was declared a Sanctuary for all game birds (HCN No.108 of 1940). This was followed in 1942 by the Bathoen Dam in the Bangwaketse Tribal Territory, all game birds being protected within a radius of 3kms of the dam (4.7km^2) (HCN No.

274 of 1942). But in 1947, wild geese, guinea-fowl, pheasants, partridges, franco-lins, the reed cormorant, whitebreasted cormorant and the South African darter, were excluded from protection in both Sanctuaries (HCN No. 115 and 116 of 1947).

In 1941, General Smuts, Governor of South Africa, requested the Resident Commissioner, Arden-Clarke, to create a sanctuary to protect a remnant herd of 40 to 50 elephant at the junction of the Shashi and Limpopo rivers, he himself having declared a sanctuary on the South African side (letter of the 14.5.1941). The request was put to Chief Tshekedi Khama of the Bamangwato, in whose Tribal Territory the land occurred[18], but he declined to agree to the proposal, stating that the elephants were already protected and shot only when they damaged plantations. Smuts asked Arden-Clarke to press the point, for concern was expressed that the land might be sold to farmers. Chief Tshekedi Khama refused to reconsider his decision, and the matter was dropped (BNA S. 159/2).

The land was eventually sold to farmers, but the elephants became so numerous that they had to be controlled, leading to the establishment of the Elephant Control Unit in 1956, and, eventually, the present-day Department of Wildlife and National Parks. Today the area forms the Mashatu private game reserve, with the elephants estimated to number 550; whereas the sanctuary on the South African side was de-gazetted for farm land soon after its establishment.

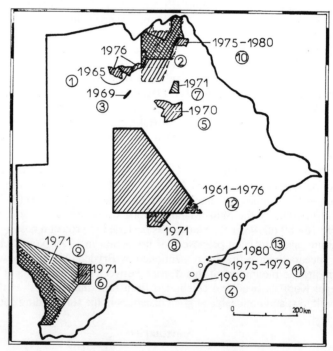

Map 6. Sanctuaries, game reserves and national parks, 1962–1980. (1) Moremi Game Reserve; (2) Chobe National Park; (3) Maun Sanctuary; (4) Naune Dam Game Reserve; (S) Makgadikgadi Pans Game Reserve; (6) Mabua-sehube Game Reserve; (7) Nxai Pan National Park; (8) Khutse Game Reserve; (9) Gemsbok National Park; (10) Maikaelelo Game Reserve; (11) Gaborone Dam National Park; (12) Portion *de facto* excised from Central Kalahari Game Reserve; (13) Gaborone Game Reserve.

In connection with the same elephants, a sanctuary was declared in the Fort Tuli area in 1948 (HCN No. 262 of 1948), but the Notice cancelled in 1951 as the area was not within Botswana (HCN No. 182 of 1951).

At Maun, an 85km² Sanctuary was declared along the Thamalakane River in 1969 (SI No. 58 of 1969).

National Parks

From 1965 to 1967, an ecological survey was conducted in the Chobe Game Reserve and adjacent areas, sponsored by the Food and Agricultural Organisation of the United Nations Development Programme. This was a follow-up of the African Special Project instituted in co-operation with the International Union for the Conservation of Nature and Natural Resources, whose first phase was the Arusha Conference in 1961 (see Part I, note 15); followed by a visit to Botswana in 1962 (Riney and Hill 1967). The survey of the Chobe Game Reserve recommended elevation of the Reserve to national park status, partly to resolve conflicts both in land use and between the Game and Forestry Departments, and to prevent further timber exploitation. Logging concessions had first been granted in the region in 1934, and the last timber extraction had taken place in 1956. Also, it was considered that the Game Reserve Regulations clearly indicated Government's intention that the area should be managed as a national park (Child 1968). As a result, Botswana's first national park was declared on the 31.8.1967 under the new National Parks Act, 1967 (Act No. 48 of 1967), the declaration coming into force on the 8.3.1968 (GN No. 64 of 1968). In effect, no declaration was issued prior to gazettement, as is called for under Sec. 4 of the National Parks Act, which presumably means that its inclusion in the Schedule was *ultra vires*.

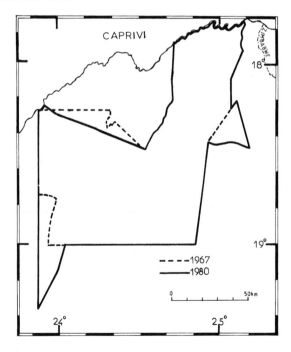

Map 7. Chobe National Park boundaries 1967–1980

The area attributed to national park status comprised the majority of the former Game Reserve, but with a reduction in size to 10,100km^2. A large settlement at Serondella, which had developed with the timber industry, was gradually removed after 1968, but it was not until 1974 that the area was finally cleared of settlement.

In 1980 further changes were made in the boundaries, which increased the area to 10,570km^2 (SI No. 126 of 1980); and in 1987 the boundaries were re-described (SI No. 9 of 1987) (Map 7).

A hotel was opened in the Reserve in 1962, and an international airport will be opened at Kasane in 1991; with its runway reaching almost to the Park entrance. Thus both Rey and Gubbins' dreams were brought to full fruition through the enthusiasm of Major Bromfield, little remembered today for his role in laying the foundations for Botswana's first national park.

When Major Bromfield was pursuing his search into a suitable area for creation as a national park, the Divisional Commissioner (North), by letter of the 28.8.1957, proposed that, in addition to the Chobe area, Nyie or "Paradise" Pan[19], an area along the Colonial Development Corporation's stock route to Kazungula, should also be a national park or 'sanctuary'. From 1966 to 1967 an ecological study of the area was conducted by Birkenholz (see above), who recommended that the Nxai Pan area be declared a national park (Birkenholz 1967). In 1970 a description of an area totalling 1,800km^2 was drawn up for gazettement as the Nxai Pan National Park, but at the last minute objection was raised by the Director of Veterinary Services to the southern boundary running along the old Kanyu-Odiakwe road. The boundary was thus redrawn along the 20°S latitude, with the area reduced to 1,500km^2; and in 1971 the area was declared a National Park (SI No. 59 of 1971). The western boundary was obliged to follow the old Bushman Pits to Pandamatenga stock route, which the Veterinary Department insisted on keeping open. This was revised in 1982, with the boundary being placed farther west and adding another 700km^2 to the Park. This extension was approved by the North West District Council in July 1982 and moves were made to gazette the new boundary in June 1983, but to date this has not been done.

In the same year that the Nxai Pan National Park was declared, the southern Game Reserve was also elevated to national park status as the Gemsbok National Park, with the area increased to 24,000km^2 (SI No. 83 of 1971). Disputes concerning the southern boundary continued until 1987, when it was re-defined by SI No. 9 of 1987. The former Game Reserve was not, however, formally de-gazetted; and a small area of 400km^2 still legally exists as Game Reserve outside of the National Park boundary.

In 1975 the Gaborone Dam National Park was declared, totalling some 3km^2 (SI No. 141 of 1975), but revoked in 1979, the area being considered as unsuitable (SI No. 155 of 1979).

Private Game Reserves

Act No. 36 of 1886 provided for the protection of game on private land if notice of intention to protect was made public (Sec. 7). This measure probably resulted from the experience of protecting the bontebok on private land in South Africa, a measure which had saved the species from extinction. In 1904, Tati Concessions Ltd., tried to invoke this provision in Botswana, their solicitors in Bulawayo issuing a statement that the Company was desirous of protecting game on its land (letter of the 13.2.1904), and would prosecute any hunters found thereon (BNA

RC.10/17). However, it was questioned whether the Company really owned the land, and no prosecutions appear to have ensued which might have established the point. Thus ownership in favour of the Company was not established until 1911 (Hailey 1953).

Although the penalty for illegal hunting on private land was increased in 1950 by 7.5 times, with the possibility of both fine and imprisonment (cap. 114), it was not until the Fauna Conservation Proclamation of 1961 that the category of Private Game Reserve was introduced (Sec. 8). Under this provision a private landholder could apply to have his land so gazetted, the penalty for illegal hunting in a Private Game Reserve being much higher than that for illegal hunting on ordinary private land; although the Proclamation had, at the same time, made it an offence to hunt on any private land without the written consent of the owner or occupier (Sec. 45). Hunting in a Private Game Reserve was prohibited except in accordance with the provisions of the gazettement, and this usually specified the retention of land-holder's privileges (the right to hunt certain species without a licence).

In the Legislative Council debate of the 26.10.1961 on the new Proclamation, some opposition was voiced to the concept of Private Game Reserves on the grounds that they could harbour infectious diseases in the middle of farming areas; but the right of the individual to do as he pleased on his own land was finally upheld. It was not, however, until 1967 that landowners availed themselves of the provision, because the amended Fauna Conservation Act (Act No. 47 of 1967) equalised the penalty for illegal hunting on private land with that on other land. This encouraged landowners to gazette their land as private game reserves in order that illegal hunters would be discouraged by the higher penalty. Thus the first Private Game Reserve was declared in 1967 (part of Sherwood Farm in the Tuli Block) (GN No. 17 of 1967), to be quickly followed by others. By 1987 there were 51 gazetted Private Game Reserves[20], but these are anomalous as protected areas since the landholders retain their hunting privileges.

Wildlife Management Areas

In 1967 Birkenholz had referred to a "management area" in his proposals for the future of the Boteti River game concentration area (Birkenholz 1967); although the area was eventually included in the Makgadikgadi Pans Game Reserve. It was not until 1974 that specific proposals for a category of land termed Wildlife Mana-gement Areas were made (Sherburne et al. 1974):
"Certain areas ... should ... be classified and gazetted as defined as those areas which are to be used for the maintenance of wildlife, including resident, subsis-tence and recreational hunting, to the exclusion of other forms of land use, particu-larly agriculture or grazing ... The main intent in establishing Wildlife Manage-ment Areas is to ensure that until long-range planning is carried out, these lands are not ruined by other land use activities that may prove to be of only short-term advantage to the people and detrimental ... The use of such lands should be periodically and carefully reviewed ... "[21]

Areas proposed as Wildlife Management Areas were to the east of the Chobe National Park; the Okavango swamps; an area around Nxai Pan National Park and the Makgadikgadi Pans Game Reserve; the southern half of the Central Kgalagadi Game Reserve; and an area between the latter and the Gemsbok National Park (Map 8a).

In a subsequent report (FAO 1977), the principle of Wildlife Management Areas was upheld, but no areas were identified. Rather the report recommended that such identification should take place. It was not until 1979 that this category of land use became a reality under statutory law and its control outlined (Act No. 1 of 1979, Fauna Conservation (Amendment) Act, 1979, Sec. 11B and 11C). Prior to this, Government had produced its Tribal Grazing Land Policy (1975), which had three main goals:

1. to improve range management and prevent overgrazing and further environmental degradation;

2. to bring about a greater equality of rural income; and

3. to foster growth and commercialisation of the livestock industry.

To achieve these aims, land was to be divided into three categories:

i. commercial land, where individuals would be given exclusive rights to areas of land which have become known as TGLP ranches;

ii. communal land, where the customary system of land occupation would remain; and

iii. reserve land, land which would not be allocated but set aside for the future, and to provide safeguards for the poorer members of the population; by which was meant the Remote Area Dwellers[22] who lived by hunting and gathering.

Hitchcock (1982) has pointed out that virtually no reserve areas were, in fact, set aside "although some people consider the proposed Wildlife Management Areas to be a kind of reserve land". But Wildlife Management Areas were not considered at all in the original Tribal Grazing Lands Policy planning process; and in the Botswana Government's fourth National Development Plan for 1976–1981 (published in 1977), some 38% of the land surface was shown as "unused" (Map 8b).

No consideration was given to the fact that this land was occupied by hunter-gatherers whose livelihood depended upon access to extensive tracts of wilderness. However, a revised land use plan, dated June 1978, provided for Wildlife Management Areas but no other reserved land, other than areas "not yet zoned" (Map 8c). Since one of the main objectives of Wildlife Management Areas, although not enunciated in the original proposition, had become that of safe-guarding animal migration routes, the isolation of the areas shown in the 1978 plan was clearly unsatisfactory; and by 1987 the Wildlife Management Areas had been extended to cover some 22.6% of the country (131,500km²), occupying some of the previously unzoned land, and also some State land. But no reserve areas as originally conceived under the TGLP, were provided for (Map 8d).

The Botswana Government's Wildlife Conservation Policy, 1986, states that reserved areas were defined in two categories under the Tribal Grazing Lands Policy: those areas reserved for future use by people with only a few cattle, and those reserved for alternative uses, such as wildlife, mining and cultivation. "The WMAs can therefore be considered as a form of zoning of land for wildlife utilisation within the Reserved Areas category as differentiated by the TGLP". The Policy goes on to state: "Wildlife Management Areas will differ from National Parks and Game Reserves in that Parks and Reserves are ... primarily preservation areas: total preservation of the resource is practised. In WMA's, on the other hand, sustained wildlife utilisation will be actively encouraged. Some WMA's adjacent to National Parks/Game Reserves will act as buffer zones to prevent conflict between the latter and areas of more intensive agricultural uses. Others will provide protection to migrating wildlife by safeguarding migratory corridors. (Sec. 3.4.1).

"Wildlife utilisation and management will be the recognised primary form of land use in these designated areas" (Sec. 3.3.8).

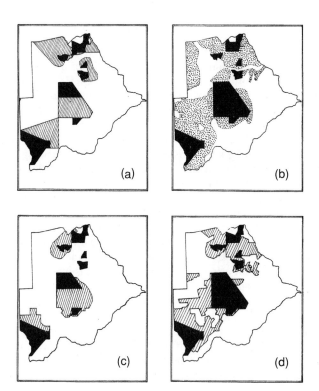

Map 8. (a) The first area proposed as Wildlife Management Areas, 1974. Blocked areas – protected areas; cross-hatched areas – areas proposed for Wildlife Management Areas. (b) Areas considered by Government as "unused", 1977. Blocked areas – protected areas; stippled areas – "unused" land. (c) Areas proposed as Wildlife Management Areas, 1978. Blocked areas – protected areas; cross-hatched areas – areas proposed for Wildlife Management Areas. (d) Areas proposed as Wildlife Management Areas, 1987. Blocked areas – protected areas; cross-hatched areas-areas proposed for Wildlife Management Areas.

Thus, as defined in the Wildlife Conservation Policy, Wildlife Management Areas have shed the flexibility of approach in the original proposal of Sherburne *et al.*, and the Policy shows an encouraging departure from that debated by the Legislative Council in 1961, whereby it was generally accepted that in the future there would be no place for game outside of the game reserves. But although a total of almost 132,000km^2 had been identified for Wildlife Management Areas in 1987, to date (1990) not a single such area has been gazetted under the Fauna Conservation Act. This is seen as due primarily to the facts that:

a) there are no other Reserved Areas set aside; and

b) the suspicion of local authorities that Wildlife Management Areas will become simply another category of national park or game reserve, where not only might hunting be forbidden, but also future grazing and settlement needs will be prevented.

Conclusion

The history of protected areas in Botswana is a relatively recent one within the concept of national parks and game reserves conforming to the African Convention. Although a significant proportion of the country's surface area has now been set aside for this purpose, exceeding that of any other country on the African continent, the nature of the environment means that relatively larger areas are required to support the same biomass, or liveweight, of game, than is the case in some other countries. Thus the biomass of game in the Kalahari region peaked around 1979 at about 400kg/km^2. This compares with an increasing biomass in the Serengeti National Park, Tanzania, in the 1970s, of some 5,200kg/km^2; or some thirteen times that of the Kalahari. Thus, the 51,800km^2 Central Kgalagadi Game Reserve is roughly equivalent to a 4,000km^2 game reserve in Tanzania.

Botswana therefore is obliged to put proportionally much greater effort into the protection of its natural resources than must a country such as, say, Tanzania. The actual size of protected areas is only relative, it is what they protect which is important; and the policy in Botswana has been the same as that of most other countries, that the areas set aside for game are those areas which are not seen at the time as being of use for any other purpose.

Botswana has two categories of protected area not found elsewhere, namely Private Game Reserves and Wildlife Management Areas. The former are not strictly preservation areas; whereas the latter somewhat resemble what are known elsewhere as "multiple use areas", differing in that whereas the latter is a form of land use zoning taking cognisance of game, Wildlife Management Areas give a priority to game usage over other forms of land use.

Figure 2 shows how the area in which game has been protected has remained remarkably consistent in size; such that in 1988, 77.5% of the peak in protected area coverage, which occurred in 1942, is still protected. The inclusion of Wildlife Management Areas would raise this figure to over 162%. The creation of a National Parks Division within the Department of Wildlife and National Parks in 1988, signifies that the Government acknowledges the importance of the role of protected areas, although it has yet to ratify the African Convention.

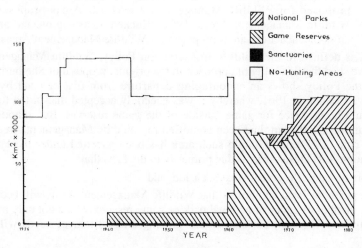

Figure 2. Changes in the sizes and categories of areas protecting game, 1926–1980 (km^2 x 1000).

1. Protected areas in Botswana are legally defi ed as areas protected for security reasons, but the term is used here in its internationally accepted sense of conservation areas.

2. The London Convention defined a National Park as: "an area (a) placed under public control, the boundaries of which shall not be altered or capable of alienation except by the competent legal authority; (b) set aside for the propagation, protection, and preservation of wild animal life and wild vegetation, and for the preservation of objects of aesthetic, geological, prehistoric, historical, archaeological, or other scientific interest for the benefit, advantage and enjoyment of the general public; (c) in which the hunting, killing, or capturing of fauna and the destruction or collection of flora is prohibited except by or under the direction of the park authorities".

3. See note Part I (15).

4. The definition of a National Park under the African Convention on the Conservation of Nature and Natural Resources, 1968, follows closely that of the London Convention, 1933, defining it as an area:

(i) under state control and the boundaries of which may not be altered or any portion alienated except by the competent legislative authority;

(ii) exclusively set aside for the propagation, protection, conservation and management of vegetation and wild animals as well as for the protection of sites, landscapes or geological formations of particular scientific or aesthetic value, for the benefit and enjoyment of the general public and,

(iii) in which the killing, hunting and capture of animals and the destruction or collection of plants are prohibited except for scientific and management purposes and on the condition that such measures are taken under the direction or control of the competent authority;

(iv) covering any aquatic environment to which all of the provisions of section (b) (i-iii) above are applicable.

5. Deer forests existed in England prior to William the Conqueror (AD1066), but such forests were not akin to game reserves as Hammersley (1960), for example, suggests; but were more like game ranches, designed to provide provender for the royal table. Thus in an average year, Henry III (*circa* 1260), took 607 fallow deer, 159 red deer, 45 roe deer and 88 wild pig (Rackham 1980). For his Christmas dinner in 1251, he had 430 red deer, 200 fallow deer, 200 roe deer, 200 wild pigs, 1300 hares, 450 rabbits, 2100 partridges, 290 pheasants, and 395 swans and other birds (Rackham 1986). Most of the animals were taken by professional huntsmen, what we would term today "game croppers". Unlike African monarchs in later centuries, the kings of England kept no vast herds of stock because of the difficulty of winter feeding. Royal forests were thus necessary to provide meat in the large quantities that a royal household would require. Rackham (1986) appears to be the first to point out that the king would have been hard put to find time to hunt in all of the 80 forests which existed in the time of Henry III.

6. Refers to an area of land sold after 1922 by the British South Africa Company to European farmers.

7. Rey refers to this in his diary entry for the 12th of February (Parsons and Crowder 1988), so clearly did not keep his diary regularly.

8. The villages and the number of families moved from each were as follows: Kyky (26); Stillasi (13); Rooipits (12); Leeudrai (9); and Hottentots camped at Union's End (BNA S. 213/6).

9. Later this authority was extended to cover the whole of the Kgalagadi District (BNA S. 108/2/5).

10. As recently as 1983 it was stated: "As far as nature conservation is concerned, the British colonial government conveyed total jurisdiction over the area to the National Parks Board of South Africa, and this arrangement is still valid" (Van Wyk and LeRiche 1984). But although the South African honorary Game Warden was formerly paid a sum to cover his expenses, the area has never been under the jurisdiction of the National Parks Board of South Africa.

11. John Gaspard Gubbins, 1877–1935. Born in England, farmed in western Transvaal. Africana collector whose collection formed the beginning of the Africana museum, Johannesburg. He was visited from time to time by Rey.

12. Hingston's requirements for a national park (actually ten) were as follows:

   "(1) A Park should contain, as far as possible, all the animal types characteristic of the country in which it lies.

   (2) A Park should be reasonably well stocked with such types.

   (3) A Park should be of adequate size. It must be large enough not only to include the animals, but also to cover the extent of their migrations.

   (4) A Park must hold a sufficiency of animal food with water and salt at all seasons of the year.

   (5) A Park ought not to contain land the development of which is essential to the territory.

   (6) A Park should preferably contain no minerals of economic value. The presence of payable minerals, however, does not necessarily rule out a Park.

   (7) A Park should contain the fewest human inhabitants possible. Where natives cultivate land in a Park complaints are certain to arise.

   (8) A Park should be accessible. Roads, rivers, railways through or near a Park are distinctly advantageous.

   (9) A Park should contain, as far as possible, natural features of scenic and geographical interest, such as mountains, lakes, forests and waterfalls.

   (10) A Park should be, if possible, healthy for human visitors and possess a comfortable climate.

13. Formerly the Sabie Game Reserve, proclaimed in 1898.

14. Presumably the person referred to by Rey in his diary as Sinvala Konguena, whom he met on the 22nd June 1930 (Parsons and Crowder 1988), real name Sinvula Nkonkwena, father of the present sub-chief at Kavimba. Munga was abandoned in the floods of 1955–58.

15. There may have been more to this than at first appears, for some anthropologists were against the proposal of a "human zoo", the integrity of which could not be guaranteed, and considered that the San should be given opportunities in training to absorb them into the modern economy (see, for example, Heinz and Lee 1978). In order not to openly oppose the Bushman Survey Officer whom they had appointed to make recommendations, Government therefore may have wished to appear to partially meet Silberbauer's proposal without, in fact, doing so at all.

16. Named after the Regent of the Tawana.

17. Aasvogel Kop = Afrikaans for "Vulture Rock".

18. This land had been formerly claimed by Chief Lobengula (d.1899) of the Matabele, as his private hunting ground.

19. This appears to have been the "Kamakama" of Livingstone, 1853, (Livingstone 1857).

20. Many of these holdings are contiguous so that there are only 17 separate blocks.

21. The term "Wildlife Management Areas" appears to have been first proposed by Dodds and Patton (1968) in their land use plan for the Luangwa Valley, Zambia.

22. Remote Area Dwellers were formerly known as "Bushmen".

Part III
History and Evolution of the Protection of Animal Species

Introduction

In Part I of this essay it has been shown that customary taboos concerning totem animals served as an early form of species' protection, but this had little relationship, if any, to the status of species. The destruction of elephant and ostrich populations in eastern Botswana by commercial hunters towards the end of the 19th century made Chiefs, whose income from these sources had suffered diminishing returns, appreciate the vulnerability of species. Thus, with the introduction of statutory law, they were prepared to co-operate with the Administration in applying protective measures. In spite of the onslaught by commercial hunters, Botswana was fortunate in losing only one known species in recent history. This was the white rhinoceros, believed to have been exterminated towards the end of last century (Smithers 1971)[1]. It has now been successfully reintroduced from South Africa.

The Game Law Amendment Act, 1886, although defining "game" , did not prohibit the hunting of any particular species; but the 1893 Proclamation expressly forbade the hunting of elephant, giraffe and eland; those species most sought after by the commercial hunters. The ostrich was also one of their target species, but this was protected by separate legislation in the form of the Ostrich Export Duty Act, 1884. The prohibition did not extend to tribesmen in their tribal areas, but, as described in the Introduction to Part I, the co-operation of the Chiefs was sought in applying it in those areas through customary law. The destruction of game by the great rinderpest epidemic of 1896–7, added urgency to the necessity to introduce restrictive laws.

Protected Species

The London Convention, 1900, listed the following genera and species which, it was agreed by the conference, should not be hunted nor destroyed:

- on account of their usefulness: vultures, the secretary bird, owls and tick birds;
- on account of their rarity and threatened extermination [species occurring in Botswana]: giraffe and eland.

Giraffe and eland were already protected under the 1893 Proclamation, but the repeal of this Proclamation by Proclamation 22 of 1904, allowed these species to be hunted under special permit; thus effectively relegating them to Schedule IV of the Convention, "animals ... of which only limited numbers may be killed". This Schedule did not list giraffe. Proclamation 5 of 1906 provided special protection for the giraffe by restricting trade in its hides and tails.

Botswana has never conformed to the requirement of the 1900 Convention, that there should be a category prohibiting hunting, but has always adopted a proviso permitting hunting under special permit or licence. In 1922, the rhinoceros (HCN No. 29 of 1922) and the hen ostrich (Proc. 14 of 1927), were added to the list of protected species; which now comprised elephant, giraffe, eland, rhinoceros and the hen ostrich. In 1925, Proclamation 17 declared these species as Royal Game (see Part I); but the High Commissioner could authorise the Resident Commissioner to issue a licence to hunt them, and in 1932 a fee for such a licence was introduced (Proc. 12), suggesting that its issue was not unusual, at least frequent enough to constitute a source of revenue.

Proclamation 53 of 1933 prohibited the destruction, capture or sale, of any wild bird not classed as "game"; the Resident Commissioner having the power to issue permits only if satisfied that the objective was for scientific or educational purposes. No exemption was made for the tribal areas. This Proclamation appears to be based on Proclamation 44 of 1914, "Plumage Birds Protection and Preservation", which prohibited the possession of, or trade in, the plumage of wild birds; which Proclamation it did not repeal, but copied *mutatis mutandis*.

The London Convention, 1933, introduced two categories of protected species:
– class 'A' animals, to be protected as completely as possible, with killing or capturing only by special permission of the highest authority, for scientific purposes or for essential administration; and
– class 'B' animals to be hunted only under special licence (Art. 8 (1)).

The Article however carried the proviso: "No hunting or other rights already possessed by native chiefs or tribes or any other persons or bodies, by treaty, concession or specific agreement, or any administrative permission in those areas in which such rights have already been definitely recognised by the authorities of the territory, are to be considered as being in any way prejudiced by the provisions of the preceding paragraph [Art. 8(1)]", (Art. 8 (2)). For Botswana, that meant that the *status quo* with respect to the Tribal Territories would not be affected by adherence to the Convention. It also carried a proviso allowing killing in defence of life or property, in time of famine, for the protection of human life, for public health, for protection of domestic stock and for any requirement relating to public order (Art. 8 (5)).

The animals affected by the Convention in Botswana were:
– class 'A': aardwolf, white rhinoceros, elephants with tusks each weighing less than 5kg.;
– class 'B': giraffe, black rhinoceros, elephants with tusks weighing more than 5kg., pangolin, marabou stork, ground hornbill, ostrich, secretary bird, little egret, great white egret, yellow-billed egret and buff-backed heron.

Significant changes were reflected in Botswana law following the signing of the Convention (Proc. 19 of 1940); the list of Royal Game species being extended, while the marabout stork, ground hornbill and egrets were classified as Large Game. But while the list of Royal Game was considerably longer than that of Class 'A' species under the Convention, birds classified as Class 'B' species, which had formerly been totally protected under Proc. 53 of 1933, now became huntable, provided a licence was granted.

A further major advance in species protection came with the 1961 Fauna Conservation Proclamation. Under this Proclamation, the Resident Commissioner could grant a permit to take Royal Game only if it was for the purposes of:
– education or scientific research;
– providing specimens for museums and similar institutions;
– providing specimens for zoological gardens and similar institutions;

– domestication, breeding or farming; or

– in the interests of the conservation, management control or utilisation of wild life.

Thus the conditions under which Royal Game could be taken became considerably limited, and the list of species was extended (Table 1). But elephant protection was only restricted to immature specimens and females, as was originally required under the Convention. Roan and sable antelope were added to the Schedule in 1952 (Proc. 3 of 1952). However, without amending the Schedule, the Fauna Conservation (Amendment) Regulations, 1965 (LN No. 20 of 1965), introduced a new type of hunting licence, termed a package licence. Category 'A' of this licence included Chobe bushbuck, roan and sable antelope, and waterbuck; all of which were Royal Game. Category 'B' of the licence also listed Chobe bushbuck and sable antelope. This was amended in 1968 by Statutory Instrument No. 19.

In 1966, the antbear and the aardwolf were added to the Schedule (LN No. 98 of 1966). In 1967 (Act. No. 47 of 1967) seven species were removed and three others added, namely the brown hyaena, pangolin and yellow-spotted dassie. The classification of Royal Game was replaced with Conserved animals (Table 1). This only applied to State land, each Tribal Territory introducing its own list of conserved species with its Tribal Territory Hunting Regulations. These are shown in Table 2, and although the tribal lists were much shorter than that of the principal law, in some cases this was a reflection of the species present in the Territory. The repeal of the the Tribal Territory Hunting Regulations in 1979, was followed by the universal application of the principal law, and although this made provision for classifying by area, this rather cumbersome provision has never been invoked.

In 1968, "otter"[2] was added to the list of conserved species (S.I. No. 16 of 1968); and in 1971 (SI No. 37 of 1971) twenty-three more genera and species, presumably in conformity with the African Convention, 1968, since eleven of these comprise Class "A" animals under the Convention.

Class 'A' species under the African Convention are those which are totally protected "... the hunting, capture or collection of specimens shall be permitted only on the authorisation in each case of the highest competent authority and only if required in the national interest or for scientific purposes". Species in Class 'B' "... shall be totally protected, but may be hunted, captured or collected under special authorisation granted by the competent authority". The "competent authority" is not defined.

Class 'A' species, in the case of Botswana, would comprise the following:

black-footed cat;
cheetah;
white rhinoceros;
all pelicans;
all storks,
hammerkops and ibises;
spoonbills, herons, egrets and bitterns;
all flamingoes;
the secretary bird;
all vultures;
lammergeyer;
crowned hawk-eagle;
all cranes;
ground hornbills.

In principle, this Class A category should replace the Conserved animals classification in a Contracting State; but although Botswana has not ratified the Convention, most of the above species were listed as "Conserved", with the exception of bitterns, the lammergeyer, the crowned hawk-eagle, ground hornbill and ibises.

In 1974 the roan antelope was re-classified as a conserved animal (SI No. 32 of 1974), having been dropped from the Schedule in 1967 (Act No. 47 of 1967); and in 1979 a further eleven species were added (Act No. 1 of 1979), comprising mostly birds, and including ibises which had been omitted in 1971 (SI No. 37 of 1971). This brings the total number of genera/species of mammals presently protected to 24, together with 23 genera/species of birds, and one reptile (python).

Partially Protected Species

Under the heading of "partially protected species" we consider those animals for which one must be in possession of a licence to hunt, kill or capture; since this restriction in itself imparts a measure of protection to a species. These animals were first defined in the Game Law Amendment Act, 1886, as "game"; namely paauw [bustard], korhaan, guinea-fowl, pheasant, partridge, grouse, dikkop, elephant, camelopard [giraffe], seacow [hippopotamus], buffalo, zebra, quagga, Burchell zebra, buck (comprehending the whole antelope species, with the exception of springbucks actually migrating, but including the gnu or wildebeest), hare and rabbit (not being coneys)"[3] (Sec. 2). This definition was replaced by the 1893 Proclamation with the term "Large Game", meaning "the wild ostrich ... Hippopotamus, Rhinoceros, Buffalo, Zebra, Quagga, and all animals of the Antelope species except Eland, Duiker and Steinbok". Although the term "quagga" was often used for zebra at this time, the text here indicates the true quagga, which did not occur in Botswana and had already been extinct elsewhere since 1863.

Proclamation 22 of 1904 amended the definition of "antelope species" to exclude the rhebuck and klipspringer as well as the steinbuck and duiker. The eland was also removed from this definition since it was fully protected. A schedule of species was first introduced into the legislation in 1911 (Proc. 42), listing small game and game birds, namely: rhebuck, klipspringer, duiker, steinbuck, hare, wild goose, wild duck, snipe, pauw (sic), black korhaan, bush korhaan, dikkop, guinea-fowl, pheasant, partridge, grouse, plover.

This Proclamation only restricted the sale of, or trade in, these species, no licence being required to hunt them. They were incorporated into a specific schedule in 1925 (Proc. 17 of 1925), when Royal Game, Large Game and Small Game Schedules were introduced; but a licence to hunt Small Game was not introduced until 1940 (Proc. 19 of 1940). Even then the holder of a Large Game licence was entitled to hunt Small Game as well.

In 1923 (Proc. 23 of 1923), an amendment to the 1904 Proclamation (Proc. 22 of 1904) was introduced allowing the temporary change of "wildebeest or any other animal" from the definition of Large Game to that of Small Game, thus permitting them to be hunted without licence. This provision was invoked for wildebeest in July 1924 (HCN No. 71 of 1924); July 1928 (HCN No. 85 of 1928); January 1930 (HCN No. 10 of 1930) and October 1935 (HCN No. 167 of 1935); for the Tuli Block. The first Notices were for one year, then in 1930 it was until further notice and included the Bamangwato Reserve and the Francistown District. This latter Notice, which came into force on the 22nd of January, was cancelled on October the 14th of the same year (HCN No. 128 of 1930); it was apparently

75

therefore a measure introduced against migrating wildebeest. Child (1972) records that there was a mass mortality of wildebeest in the east of the country about 1930–31, particularly at Francistown, following a long period of drought. The application of the legislation to the Tuli Block suggests that wildebeest formerly migrated eastwards to the Limpopo River. The 1935 Notice for the Tuli Block was not cancelled until September 1938 (HCN No. 145 of 1938). It had resulted from complaints from the farming community to put the wildebeest back on the Small Game Schedule, one farm (African Ranches) claiming that 600 wildebeest had recently been shot on the farm and 2,000 still remained, while cattle had to be sold because of lack of grazing (Rey 2.10.1935, BNA S. 47/9)[4]. In 1939 the measure was applied to wildebeest in the Bakgatla Reserve (HCN No. 121 of 1939), and in 1941 to part of the Kgalagadi District (HCN No. 189 of 1941), with an amendment to the latter area in 1942 (HCN No. 37 of 1942). These latter Notices coincided with a massive southerly migration of wildebeest across the Molopo River into South Africa in 1941 (Fourie and Snyman 1942), similar migrations having apparently taken place in 1927, 1935 and 1937. In 1942 the Notice was again applied to the Bakgatla Reserve, and also to the Tati District (HCN No. 196 of 1942), although the 1939 Notice for the Bakgatla Reserve had not been cancelled. In 1953 the measure was applied countrywide (HCN No. 70 of 1953), probably in connection with new moves to develop the beef cattle industry, as veterinary cordon fences were now being planned across the country following a foot and mouth disease epidemic in 1948. But, despite some opposition, in 1961 policy was changed (see Part II, Introduction), and the wildebeest became classified as a game licence animal under the Fauna Conservation Proclamation, 1961; but farmers were empowered to destroy game animals which were damaging their crops or installations (Sec. 41), a provision which exists in current law.

The provision of declaring Large Game to be Small Game, was also applied to the kudu in 1935 in the Francistown District (HCN No. 166 of 1935).

In contrast to the above, the same provision was invoked to confer protection on species by elevating them from the status of "Small Game" to that of "Large Game". Thus the springbok was classified as Large Game in the Bamangwato and Batawana Reserves in 1941 (HCN No. 189 of 1941); the following year in the Bakgatla Reserve, the Bangwaketse Reserve and the Tati District (HCN No. 196 of 1942); and in 1944 in the Lobatse District Crown lands (HCN No. 26 of 1944). In 1952 the species was classified as Large Game countrywide (HCN No. 117 of 1952), evidence of a growing concern for the decline in a species which, at the turn of the century, had existed in incredible numbers. In 1961, Chief Bathoen of the Bangwaketse, was reported as hating anyone, African or European, to shoot springbok in the Tribal Territory, where they were known as The Chief's Goats (Mathers, A.N.W. to Admin. Secretary 11.9.1961, BNA S. 584/3).

Other species, upon which protection was conferred by classifying them as Large Game, were the klipspringer in the Bakwena Reserve in 1941 (HCN No. 189 of 1941), and in the Bangwaketse District in 1942 (HCN No. 196 of 1942); and the impala in the Gaberones District in 1942 (HCN No. 196 of 1942). Both impala and springbok had been classified as Small Game in 1940 (Proc. 19 of 1940), having formerly been classed as Large Game (Proc. 17 of 1925).

Concern was expressed in South Africa in 1936 at the destruction of the matloutsie or Cape long-haired jackal (bat-eared fox) in Botswana, the skins being exported to South Africa. Protective legislation was considered, but the Chief

Agricultural Officer was of the opinion that fur-bearing animals had increased in the Protectorate in the past decade, little trapping having taken place because of a foot and mouth disease epidemic which had lowered the price of skins (BNA S.166/3). No restrictions were placed on the hunting of this species until 1967 (SI No. 25 of 1967).

In 1930 a number of birds was added to the Schedule of Large Game, and the "paauw" was defined, as follows (HCN No. 105 of 1940):

crowned crane, wattled crane, giant bustard, Ludwig's bustard, Stanley's bustard, secretary bird, ground hornbill.

Further species were added in 1940 (Proc. 19 of 1940), namely:

marabout stork, great egret, little white egret, yellowbilled egret, cattle egret, owls, yellow-billed oxpecker, red-billed oxpecker, cuckoos, rollers, orioles, vultures, greater flamingo, lesser flamingo, ibises, storks.

The hippopotamus was omitted from the Schedule of Large Game in the above Proclamation (Proc. 19 of 1940), presumably in error, and re-instated by HCN No. 105 of 1940.

By classifying many of these species as Large Game, which meant that they could be hunted on licence, this Proclamation failed to implement the agreement of the 1933 Convention, which while superseding the 1900 Convention's provision that certain species which were "useful" should be totally protected, (specifically listing vultures, owls and tick birds); listed species which it declared the protection of was of "special urgency and importance". Several of those species listed as "Large Game" were "Class B" species under the Convention which "while not requiring such rigorous protection as those mentioned in Class A, shall not be hunted, killed or captured, even by natives, except under special licence granted by the competent authorities. For this purpose a special licence shall denote a licence other than an ordinary game licence" (Art. 8 (1)). All of the birds now placed on the Schedule of Large Game, had been previously protected under the Wild Birds Protection and Preservation Proclamation, 1933 (Proc. 53 of 1933) as long as they were not classified as "game". In terms of the protection of birds, therefore, Proclamation 19 of 1940 was a retrograde step. As far as mammals were concerned, the rhebuck was transferred from Small Game to Large Game as the Rooi and the Vaal rhebuck (that is, the mountain reedbuck and the rhebok). Dropped from the Schedule was the quagga, which had now been extinct for 77 years; and the nyala, inserted into the Schedule in 1925, which did not occur in Botswana[5].

The 1940 Small Game Schedule replaced the rhebuck with the Sharpe's grysbok, a rare species known only in the extreme northeast of the country; "hare" was identified as three species: Cape, rock and red; and "wild goose" was identified as spur-winged, egyptian and pygmy goose. The dikkop was identified as the common dikkop and the water dikkop.

In 1941, ibis, storks (Large Game) and geese and wild duck (Small Game), were protected for a period of three years in the Bakgatla Reserve (HCN No. 42 of 1941); the Notice not applying to tribesmen of the Reserve.

In the Tuli Block, hartebeest, tsessebe and waterbuck, were protected in 1948 for three years (HCN No. 86 of 1948), indicative of the decline of these species in that area.

Act No. 47 of 1967, introduced a new category of protection which has subsequently caused much confusion, namely that of "Protected game". This comprised: Chobe bushbuck, defassa waterbuck, eland, elephant (immature specimens and females), klipspringer, aardwolf, rhebok, roan and sable antelope;

all species which were removed from the "Conserved animals" Schedule. This meant that these animals could now be hunted on licence, but there was a heavier penalty for illegally hunting them compared with other game animals. A result has been that from time to time offenders have been charged with the illegal hunting of protected game, when the species has been simply a "game animal" (see, for example, State vs Diseko, RC No. 585 of 1986; State vs Thupu, RC No. 605 of 1986). In 1968 (SI No. 16 of 1968) waterbuck, klipspringer and rhebok, were removed from the list, while the elephant definition was re-defined as "elephant cows with calves at foot" (revoked in 1982 by SI No. 72 of 1982). The waterbuck became a "Game licence animal", while the klipspringer was retained as a Conserved animal. The rhebok did not occur in Botswana[6]. The leopard was added in 1974 (SI No. 32 of 1974). The classification of Game birds was extended to include green pigeons and turtle doves.

The application of the principal law countrywide following Independence in 1966 (see Part I), was effected by the drawing-up of Regulations for hunting on State land and for each Tribal Territory. SI No. 25 of 1967 made the hunting in Kgalagadi and Ghanzi Districts by indigenous residents illegal without a licence for the following species: bat-eared fox, cheetah, eland, gemsbok, giraffe, kudu, leopard lion and springbok. Whereas cheetah and giraffe were already Conserved animals, the bat-eared fox had hitherto not been a scheduled species and was hunted freely for its fur. As with "Tribally conserved animals", each Tribal Territory produced its own list of "Tribally protected game" (Table 3). Those species not listed as either Tribally conserved or Tribally protected, were hunted freely by tribesmen within their own tribal area. But under SI No. 23 of 1968, each Tribal Territory should have been set a quota based on each Controlled Hunting Area (see Part I) (Reg. 5 (1)); but until 1979 quotas were, in fact, set only for non-residents. These quotas were determined each year based mainly, it would appear, on demand, since the numbers of species were only guessed at. Von Richter and Butynksi (1973) estimate that for 1971, a total of 133, 345 animals were sold to tribal hunters, of which 50,379 were shot. With the revocation of the State and Tribal Hunting Regulations in 1979 (see Part I), a single list of "Protected species" was drawn up and applied countrywide (Table 4); and the Unified Hunting Regulations, 1979 (SI No. 9 of 1979) introduced a countrywide quota system, published annually as a Government Notice, "Determination of the Chief Game Warden". Table 5 shows the numbers allowed on licence for the years 1979 to 1987, although this does not indicate the number actually sold. Nor does it include Special Game Licences, Minister's licences and ration licences.

This instrument, the quota system, can be used for the protection of species by the Chief Game Warden (Director) simply issuing a zero quota; as was the case with elephant in 1983 (GN No. 108 of 1983), although the decision to stop elephant hunting was made by Cabinet.

The Destruction of Species

The Fauna Conservation Proclamation of 1961 (Proc. 22), dispensed with the categories of Large and Small Game, replacing them with the single category "Game animals", subdivided into Game birds and Game licence animals. It also introduced a new category, "vermin", which applied to baboon, black-backed jackal, hyaena and hunting dog. These species could be freely destroyed outside of protected areas, or on private land with the landowner's permission. The brown hyaena was excluded from the category in 1967 (Act No. 47 of 1967).

The London Convention of 1900 had provided a Schedule (V) of "harmful animals ... of which it is desired to reduce the numbers within sufficient limits". These animals were given as lion; leopard; hyaenas; hunting dog; otter; baboons "and other harmful monkeys"; large birds of prey, except vultures, the secretary bird and owls; crocodiles; poisonous snakes and pythons. In addition, Sec. 15 of Art. II, committed parties to the destruction of the eggs of crocodiles, poisonous snakes and pythons. No specific application was made in Botswana of these requirements prior to 1961, but it has influenced the approach to species' conservation to this day, particularly in regard to such species as the hunting dog. The category of vermin was repealed in 1979 (Act No. 1 of 1979), the animals becoming game licence animals.

Conclusion

As concluded in Part I, the law relating to fauna conservation in Botswana is essentially a hunting law, but the provision in the Fauna Conservation Act, 1979, that "no person shall hunt or capture any animal except under and in accordance with the terms and conditions of a licence or a permit granted under this Act:

Provided that a citizen of Botswana may hunt any unscheduled animal for consumption by himself or his dependents without a licence or permit" (Sec. 15 (1)), provides a blanket cover for the protection of all vertebrate species as far as non-citizens are concerned. The intention was probably to control the commercial exploitation of "lesser" species, e.g. small birds; although the reason why all non-citizens, a minority group, should not hunt unscheduled species is not clear.

The addition, or conversely, the deletion, of a species to or from a protected list, is indicative of the changing status of a species, or the potential threat to it, e.g. unsustainable exploitation. It is significant that, as a hunting law, the list of Conserved animals has steadily increased. In international terminology, species requiring legislative protection would be regarded as endangered, vulnerable or rare"[7]. Under such a classification, only the rhinoceroses would be endangered, and most of the other Conserved animals would be rare; with the exception of the giraffe, which is a common species. But increased biological knowledge would no doubt serve to enlarge the list of rare species, particularly with regard to reptiles and amphibians. However, these latter animals are not hunted, and the law has yet to address the problem of conservation *per se*, as evinced by the fact, for example, that invertebrates are given no protection at all. Undoubtedly more species will enter the endangered species list in Botswana in the not-too-distant future; but overall we should witness a two-pronged approach in future legislative trends. One of these will be towards the commercial use of game, while the other will be towards true nature conservation law as opposed to hunting law; with many small species of vertebrate being given protection and logically embracing invertebrate species as well. In this respect the legislation will come closer to current European legislation than is present law. South African law lists a number of butterflies under the schedule of "Ordinary Game" for the Transvaal; while in order to accommodate the provisions of the Washington Convention, 1973 (CITES), a schedule of "Endangered and Rare Species" includes all mammals, birds, reptiles, amphibians, fish and molluscs so listed under the Convention, whether they exist in Africa or not. Similar legislation applies to the Orange Free State and to Natal. The history of game law in Botswana shows that hunting laws were accepted and understood when introduced as statutory law, even although there may have been objections;

but the concept of preserving living creatures which have no apparent utility is of a more alien nature and has yet to be endorsed.

The increased rarity of species comes not from hunting alone, although this factor is a major one in Botswana, but also from the loss of habitat, as in the case of the tsessebe; from the loss of essential habitat, e.g. access to water, as in the case of the wildebeest; and other factors, such as poisoning by insecticides, in the case of small species. When game animals have become sufficiently rare that they can no longer be hunted, what had its genesis as a hunting law, will become by default a nature conservation law. Thus, unless the hunting law is sufficiently strong, its natural evolution must be towards protection, and any weakening of its impact serves to accelerate this process.

Von Richter and Passineau (1979) concluded in 1976 that only the white rhinoceros was "threatened with extinction" in Botswana; eleven species were "rare", and all other species, including those receiving special protection, were "safe". The authors gave three main reason to account for this "relatively fortunate situation". Firstly, prior to the last few decades, the impact of man on wild animals and their habitats had been relatively insignificant compared to that occurring in other countries. Secondly, vulnerable species can be gazetted as Conserved animals; and thirdly, a cross-section of the major habitat types is protected as national parks and game reserves "thus ensuring that rare and endangered species will continue to have adequate refuges for their survival".

In spite of this, the rate of decline of many species has accelerated in recent years, due to a combination of drought and changes in land use, as well as the increased accessibility to formerly remote areas by both legal and illegal hunters. Today, the black rhinoceros is more threatened with extinction than is the white; but it is those species which formerly occurred in large numbers due to their ability to migrate in search of water and food, which are now at greatest risk. Species like wildebeest, hartebeest, eland and tsessebe, are those most likely to become rare in the future. While already rare species like the puku, continue to decline in numbers.

The law governing the protection of species has seen little change since its inception, only the lists of species concerned increasing with time. To that extent species' protection laws fail in their primary objective of arresting a decline in species numbers, but they nevertheless serve to retard the process of the extinction of a species which would take place in the absence of such laws. Botswana may have witnessed a "relatively fortunate situation" in the past, in the words of von Richter and Passineau, but those circumstances have changed to the extent that effective laws will be more than ever necessary in the future.

Notes to Part III

1. The black rhinoceros is now on the verge of extinction in Botswana.

2. Otters occurring in Botswana are the spotted-necked otter *Lutra macucollis* and the Cape clawless otter *Aonyx capensis*.

3. Coney was the Old English term for rabbit, frequently used in English law. In this definition it refers to the hyrax.

4. A letter dated 1938 on the subject of wildebeest destruction stated that hunting them did not pay unless one could shoot 40 per week, one hunter having shot 82 in 14 days. The method used was to follow the herds, shooting as many as one

could. A hunter on African Ranches in the Tuli Block, manufactured 2, 0001bs of biltong, making 5001bs per trip, or 300 to 5001bs per month (BNA S.47/9).

5. There have been recent reports (1986) of odd sightings of the nyala *Tragelaphus angasi* along the Limpopo River. These animals originate from the northern Transvaal where the species has been introduced outside of its recent natural range.

6. Shortridge (1934) considered that the rhebok *Pelea capreolus* formerly occurred in hilly country around Gaborone, but this has never been confirmed. The species occurs in the western Transvaal.

7. The International Union for the Conservation of Nature and Natural Resources (IUCN) definitions are as follows:

   – endangered: taxa in danger of extinction and where survival is unlikely if the causal factors continue;

   – vulnerable: taxa believed likely to become endangered in the near future if causal factors continue;

   – rare: taxa with small populations which are not at present endangered or vulnerable, but which are at risk.

References

Aguda, A. (1973). "Legal development in Botswana from 1885 to 1966", *Botswana Notes and Records* 5:52–63 (Botswana Society, Gaborone).

Birkenholz, D.E. (1967). "A study of the status and movements of big game in the Botletle-Nyai Pan area of Botswana". pp 1–19 typescript.

Blackstone, W.(1765–9). *Commentaries on the Laws of England*. 4 vols. (A. Strahan: London).

BLR. (1982). (1). (Government Printer: Gaborone).

BNA RC.10/17.

BNA S. 47/9.

BNA S. 108/2/1.

BNA S. 108/2/2.

BNA S. 108/2/3.

BNA S. 108/2/5.

BNA S. 157/6.

BNA S. 159/2.

BNA S. 166/1.

BNA S. 166/2.

BNA S. 166/3.

BNA S. 169/6.

BNA S. 213/6.

BNA S. 213/7/1.

BNA S. 238/14.

BNA S. 238/15.

BNA S. 238/16.

BNA S. 553/12.

BNA S. 568/13/1.

BNA S. 584/1

BNA S. 584/3.

Bothma, J. and Rabie, A. (1983). "Wild Animals", in *Environmental Concerns in South Africa,* eds Fuggle, R.A. & Rabie, A., pp. 190-236. (Capetown: Juta & Co.Ltd.).

Brewer, I.G.(1974). "Sources of the criminal law of Botswana". *J.A.L.* 18:24–36.

Bryden, H.A.(1893). *Gun and Camera in Southern Africa.* (Edward Stanford: London).

Burn, R. (1785). *The Justice of the Peace and Parish Officer.* 4 vols. (London).

Campbell, A.C. (1973). "The National Park and Reserve System in Botswana", *Biol. Cons.* 5: 7-14.

Campbell, A.C.(1980). "Some aspects of traditional wildlife utilisation in Botswana", in *Wildlife Management and Utilisation.* Proceedings of the Fifth Regional Wildlife Conference for Eastern and Central Africa. pp. 151–161. (Govt. Printer: Gaborone).

Child, G. (1968). *An Ecological Survey of Northeastern Botswana.* (UNDP/FAO: Rome).

Child, G. (1972). "Observations on a wildebeest die-off in Botswana". *Arnoldia,* 5(31): 1-13.

Chitty, J. (1812). *A Treatise on the Game Laws and on Fisheries.* (W. Clarke & Son.: London).

Christian , E. (1817). *A Treatise on the Game Laws.* (W.Clarke & Sons:London).

Davies, J.E. (n.d.). *The History of Tsetse Fly Control in Botswana.* (Govt. Printer: Gaborone).

Dawson, G. (1694). *Origo legum: or a Treatise of the Origin of Laws.* (Richard Chiswell: London).

Dodds, D.G. and Patton, D.R. (1968). *"Wildlife and Land–Use Survey of the Luangwa Valley. Report to the Government of Zambia".* (FAO: Rome).

Egharevba, J.U. (1946). *Benin Laws and Customs.* (Service Press: Lagos).

Elias, T.O. (1956). *The Nature of African Customary Law.* (Manchester University Press: Manchester).

FAO. (1977). *Wildlife Management and Utilisation, Botswana. Project findings and recommendations.* (FAO/UNDP: Rome).

Fourie, J.M. and Snyman, P.S. (1942). "Blouwildebeesoog". *Jl.S.A.V.M.A.* XIII: 43-47.

Galland, Y. (1986). *"Report drawn up on behalf of the Committee on Development and Co-operation on the disturbance of the ecological balance in Botswana".* (European Communities European Parliament Working Documents, 1986-7: Brussels).

Garmonsway, G.M. (1953). trans. *The Anglo-Saxon Chronicle.* (Dent:London).

Gillon, J-L. and Villepin, G.de. (1844). *Nouveau Code des Chasses.* (Librairie Administrative de Paul Dupont: Paris).

Gott vs Measures. (1947). (1 KB 1948).

Government of Botswana. (1975). *Government Paper No.2 of 1975 National Policy on Tribal Grazing Land.* (Govt. Printer: Gaborone).

Government of Botswana. (1986). *Government Paper No.1 of 1986 Wildlife Conservation Policy.* (Govt. Printer: Gaborone).

Greyling, I.F. (1984). "Legal aspects of the ownership of game", in *Workshop on the Conservation and Utilisation of Wild Life on Private Land,* pp.3-6. (South African Wildlife Management Association:Pretoria).

Hailey, Lord. (1953). *Native Administration in the British African Territories. Part V. The High Commission Territories: Basutoland. The Bechuanaland Protectorate and Swaziland.* (London: HMSO).

Hailey, Lord. (1956). *An African Survey.* (London: Oxford University Press).

Hammersley, G.(1960). "The revival of the forest laws under Charles I", *History.* 45 :85–102.

Hingston, R.W.G. (1930). "Report on a mission to East Africa for the purpose of investigating the most suitable methods of ensuring the preservation of its indigenous fauna ". *J. Soc. Pres. Fauna Emp.* NS XII:21–57.

Hitchcock, R.K. (1978). "Kalahari Cattle Posts: A Regional Study of Hunter-Gatherers, Pastoralists and Agriculturalists in the Western Sandveld Region, Central District, Botswana". (Govt. Printer: Gaborone).

Hitchcock, R.K. (1982). "Tradition, Social Justice and Land Reform in Central Botswana, in *Land Reform in the Making: Tradition. Public Policy and Ideology in Botswana.* ed. R.P. Werbner. pp. 1–34. (Rex Collings: London).

Judicial Circular. (1976). RM2 RM22.

Judicial Circular. (1981). No. 2.

Judicial Circular. (1985). RM 64 I (63).

Kallen, H.M. (1964). "Innovation", in *Social Change:Sources. Patterns and Consequences,* eds. Etzioni, A. and Etzioni, E. (Basic Books: New York).

Khama, S. (1971). Traditional attitudes to land and management of property with special reference to cattle". in *Proceedings of the Conference on Sustained Production from Semi-Arid Areas. Botswana Notes and Records,* Special Edition No. 1. pp. 57–61. (Botswana Society: Gaborone).

Lee, R.W. (1944). *The Elements of Roman Law with a Translation of the Institutes of Justinian.* (Sweet & Maxwell: London).

Livingstone, D. (1857). *Missionary Travels and Researches in South Africa.* (John Murray: London).

Main, M. (1987). *Kalahari. Life's Variety in Dune and Delta.* (Southern Book Publishers: Johannesburg).

Maine, H.S. (1861). *Ancient Law.* (John Murray: London).

Manwood, J. (1598). *A Treatise on the Laws of the Forest.* (Societie of Stationers: London).

Matsetse, P.M. (1986). "Ministry of Commerce and Industry Circular No.1 of 1986". (Ministry of Commerce and Industry: Gaborone).

Meek, C.K. (1946). *Land Law and Custom in the Colonies.* (Oxford University Press: London).

Molokomme, A. (1985). "The reception and development of Roman-Dutch Law in Botswana". *Lesotho Law* J.1:121–134.

Mordi, R. (1987). *"Public Attitudes Toward Wildlife in Botswana".* (Unpublished D.Phil. thesis: Yale University).

Munsche, P.B. (1981). *Gentlemen and Poachers.* (Cambridge University Press: Cambridge).

Pain, J.H. (1978). "The reception of English Roman-Dutch Law in Africa with reference to Botswana, Lesotho and Swaziland", *Comparative and International Law Journal of Southern Africa* XI:137–167 (The Institute of Foreign and Comparative Law: Pretoria).

Parsons, Q.N. (1969). "Game preservation - Is it "alien science" bestowed by Euro-peans?" *Kutlwano:* 8(3):10–11, (4):2-3,7.

Parsons, N. and Crowder, M. (1988). eds. *Monarch of All I Survey. Bechuanaland Diaries 1929–1937 by Sir Charles Rey.* (The Botswana Society: Gaborone).

Partridge, E. (1969). *Usage and Abusage.* (Penguin Books: London).

Pilane, D.L., Hartland–Rowe, R.C.B., Moepeng,T., Moroka, D.N., Ntseane,P.G., Swartz, J.K., Tshweneyagae, M. and Zimmerman, I. (1985). *Report of the Central Kgalagadi Game Reserve Fact Finding Mission.* (Govt. Printer: Gaborone).

Pim, A. (1933). *Financial and Economic Position of the Bechuanaland Protectorate.* (HMSO: London).

Pitman, C.R.S. (1934). *A report on a faunal survey of Northern Rhodesia with especial reference to game, elephant control and national Parks.* (Govt. Printer: Livingstone).

Probert, W. (1823). *The Ancient Laws of Cambria.* (London).

Rabie, A. (1973). Wildlife conservation and the law. *Comparative and International Law Journal of Southern Africa.* VI:145–198 (The Institute of Foreign and Comparative Law: Pretoria).

Rackham, O. (1980). *Ancient woodland: its history. vegetation and uses in England.* (Edward Arnold: London).

Rackham, O. (1986). *The History of the Countryside.* (J.M. Dent: London).

Roberts, S. (1969). *A Restatement of Kgatla Law Relating to Land and Natural Resources.* (Govt. Printer: Gaborone).

Riney, T. and Hill, P. (1967). *Conservation and Management of African Wildlife.* English-speaking country reports. (FAO: Rome).

du Saussay, C. (1980). *Legislation on Wildlife. Hunting and Protected Areas in some European Countries,* (FAO: Rome).

du Saussay, C. (1984). *Legislation on Wildlife and Protected Areas in Africa.* (FAO: Rome).

Schapera, I. (1938). *A Handbook of Tswana Law and Custom.* (International African Institute: London).

Schapera, I. (1943). *Native Land Tenure in the Bechuanaland Protectorate.* (Alice: South Africa).

Schapera, I. (1943a). *Tribal Legislation among the Tswana of the Bechuanaland Protectorate.* (Athlone Press: London).

Schapera, I. (1970). *Tribal Innovators: Tswana Chiefs and Social Change 1795-1940.* (Athlone Press: London).

Sherburne, J., McLaughlin, J. and Davis, R. (1974). *"A report on wildlife utilisation in Botswana".* (AWLF: Washington).

Shortridge, G.C. (1934). *The Mammals of South West Africa.* 2 vols. (Heinemann: London).

Silberbauer, G.B. (1965). *Bushman Survey Report.* (Govt. Printer: Gaberones).

Silberbauer, G.B. (1981). *Hunter and Habitat in the Central Kalahari Desert.* (Cambridge University Press: Cambridge).

Sillery, A. (1952). *The Bechuanaland Protectorate.* (Oxford University Press: London).

Smithers, R.H.N. (1971). *The Mammals of Botswana.* Museum Memoir No.4. (Trustees National Museums of Rhodesia: Salisbury).

State vs Modibetsane and Modibetsane. (1982). *Botswana Law Reports.* (Govt. Printer: Gaborone).

State vs Masedi. (1980). *Botswana Law Reports.* (Govt. Printer: Gaborone).

State vs Putter and Putter.(1974). *Botswana Law Reports.* (Govt. Printer: Gaborone).

State vs Mosinyi and Others. (1972). *Botswana Law Reports.* (Govt. Printer: Gaborone).

Tabler, E.C. (1960). *Zambesia and Matabeleland in the Seventies.* (Chatto and Windus: London).

Tennant, L.D. (1971). *Report of the Department of Wildlife and National Parks 1969-1970.* (Govt. Printer: Gaborone).

Thompson, A.C. (1959). *Laws of the Bechuanaland Protectorate*. (HMSO: London).

Tlou, T. (1985). *A History of Ngamiland –1750 to 1906 – The Formation of an African State*. (Macmillan Botswana: Gaborone).

Van Wyk, P. and LeRiche, E.A.N. (1984). "The Kalahari Gemsbok National Park: 1931-1981" . In: *Supplement to Koedoe*. (National Parks Board of Trustees: Pretoria).

von Richter, W. (1976). *"The National Parks and Game Reserve System of Botswana"* . (FAO/UNDP/DWNPT: Gaborone).

von Richter, W. and Butynski, T. (1973). "Hunting in Botswana". *Botswana Notes and Records*. 5: 191-208.

von Richter, W. and Passineau, J. (1979). "Endangered wildlife species in Botswana". *Botswana Notes and Records*. 11:121–5.

Wilson, M. and Thompson, L. (1982). *A History of South Africa to 1870*. (David Philip: Cape Town).

Woodbine, G. (1915–22). ed. *Bracton, H. de. De Legibus et Consuetudinibus Angliae*. 2 vols.

Acknowledgements

I am most grateful to Professor A. Rabie for providing me with photocopies of the Cape *placaaten*, and to J.M. van Wijk Nieuwpoort for translating them. I also wish to thank Alec Campbell for his helpful comments on the manuscript, and Mr. K.T. Ngwamotsoko, the Office of the President for permission to publish and IUCN/WWF for their generous assistance in financing the publication.

Appendix I

ACT
For the Better Preservation of Game

Whereas it is expedient to consolidate and amend the laws relating to game: Be it therefore enacted by the Governor of the Cape of Good Hope, with the advice and consent of the Legislative Council and House of Assembly thereof:-

1. The following Game Law Proclamations are hereby repealed; that is to say, the Proclamation dated 21st March, 1822, entitled Game Law Proclamation; the Proclamation dated 23rd August, 1822, entitled Amendment of "Game Law-Elephants;" and the Proclamation dated 14th March, 1823, entitled "Amendment of Game Law-Elands".

2. The word "game" shall for the purposes of this Act, be taken and understood to mean and comprehend the several birds and animals of this Colony following, not being domesticated, commmonly known as paauw, korhaan, guinea-fowl, pheasant, partridge, grouse, and dikkop, elephant, camelopard, seacow (hippopotamus), buffalo, zebra, quagga, Burchell zebra, buck (comprehending the whole antelope species, with the exception of springbucks actually migrating, but including the gnu or wildebeest) hare and rabbit (not being coneys); and the words "game licence" shall, for the purposes of this Act be taken and understood to mean a game licence duly issued by Government.

3. It shall be lawful for the Governor, by proclamation to be by him issued, to fix and prescribe for each district in this Colony, the close time or fence seasons within which it shall not be lawful to kill, pursue, hunt, or shoot at, the different kinds of game respectively within such district either with or without a game licence respectively, or with or without the landowner's permission.

4. No person shall, save as is hereinafter provided, kill, catch, capture, pursue, hunt or shoot at, sell, hawk, or expose for sale, game in any part of this Colony, without having previously obtained a game licence, under the penalty of not exceeding thirty shillings sterling for the first offence, and not exceeding five pounds sterling for every subsequent offence, excepting herefrom any game found injuring crops in cultivated lands or gardens. No person, however, shall be at liberty to pursue, shoot, kill, destroy, or capture any elephant, hippopotamus, buffalo, eland, koodoo, hartebeest, bontebok, blesbok, gemsbok, rietbok, zebra, quagga, Burchell zebra or any gnu or wildebeest of either variety, without having obtained a special permission to that effect from the Governor, under a penalty of not exceeding ten pounds sterling for each offence, or, on failure of payment thereof, not exceeding one month's imprisonment with or without hard labour: Provided, however, that landed proprietors and persons authorised by them shall, without having such special permission, be at liberty to shoot elephant upon the property of such landed proprietors.

5. No person shall kill, pursue, or shoot at game in any district in the Colony during the close time, or shall possess, sell, hawk, or expose for sale game in such district after the expiration of one week from the commencement of the close time which shall be proclaimed for any such district, under a penalty of four pounds sterling for the first offence, and eight pounds sterling for every subsequent offence.

6. No person shall, without special permission of the Governor, for purposes to

be mentioned in such permission as hereinafter is provided, at any time wilfully take away, disturb or destroy eggs, or sell, hawk, or expose for sale, or shall purchase eggs of any game birds in any part of this Colony, under the penalty of any sum not exceeding four pounds sterling for the first offence, and not less than eight pounds sterling, nor exceeding ten pounds sterling for every subsequent offence; and the said eggs shall be confiscated to Government in whose custody soever the same may at any time be found, and may be seized *brevi manu* by any land-owner, occupier of land, justice of the peace, field-cornet, constable, or police officer: Provided, always, that it shall be lawful for the Governor to permit under his hand any fit or proper person or persons to take, or carry away the eggs of any game bird, or the young of any game, whether bird or other game, for the purpose of rearing or breeding the same, or for the purpose of acclimatization or scientific investigation: and any person so obtaining the Governor's written permission as aforesaid may himself obtain or take the said eggs, birds, or animals: provided, always, that such writing shall distinctly state the number and denomination of such eggs, birds, or animals, which the holders are employed to obtain or take, which shall collectively not exceed the number specified by the Governor's permission aforesaid. And any person obtaining or taking a greater number of other kinds of such eggs, birds, or animals than those specified in the Governor's permission as aforesaid, or giving or affecting to give any person or persons authority to take or obtain, together with what he shall himself take or obtain in the whole, more than the number or other than the kinds specified in such permission as aforesaid, shall be held guilty of wilfully taking all such young or eggs as he shall have taken or obtained, or shall have given or affected to give authority in the whole to take or obtain.

7. No person shall at any time, either with or without a game licence, kill, catch, capture, pursue, hunt, or shoot at any game on any lands within this Colony, without the permission of the owner of such lands, if private property, under the penalty of any sum not exceeding five pounds sterling for the first offence, and not exceeding ten pounds sterling for every subsequent offence, in addition to any penalty, if any, to which he may be liable under any other section of this Act, the penalty provided by this section to be paid to the owner of the land; but any permission given by such owner after the event with reference to the offence shall be as valid as if given before the offence. But no penalty under this section shall in any case be enforced unless notice and warning shall have been given, either personally or by letter, or in the Gazette, or in a local newspaper, by the owner that he is desirous to preserve the game thereon.

8. Whenever any person shall be charged with killing, or capturing, pursuing, hunting, or shooting at, selling, hawking or exposing for sale game, in any part of the Colony without a licence, and shall allege in defence that such game was injuring crops in cultivated lands or gardens, the proof of the truth of such allegation shall be with the person charged.

9. In any case prosecuted under this Act every game animal shall be presumed to have been wild until shown to have been domesticated.

10. The several fines above mentioned may be recovered by any person, on behalf as well as of himself as of the Crown, in all cases where the fine shall not exceed twenty-five pounds sterling, in the Court of the Resident Magistrate of the district where the offence may have been committed, and in other cases in the Supreme Court, the Court of the Eastern Districts or the High Court of Griqualand, as the case may be, or the Circuit Court for the district where the offence may have

been committed; and a moiety of any fine imposed upon any offender, on conviction, for contravening any of the provisions of this Act, shall, save as is hereinbefore otherwise specially provided, be paid to the person on whose information such conviction shall have taken place, provided such person be not an accessory.

11. It shall be lawful for the Governor, by proclamation in the Gazette, to proclaim and declare as to any parts of this Colony that any bird or animal, to be specified in such proclamation, shall be protected and not destroyed for any number of years not exceeding three, to be mentioned in such proclamation, and also to extend to any such bird or other animal the protection of this Act, as if the same were included among the game animals in this Act defined, or to extend to any such bird or other animal the protection of such of the provisions of this Act as may be specified in such proclamation, as if such bird or other animal were expressly protected by name in such provision respectively; and also from time to time to revoke, alter, or amend such proclamation.

12. It shall be lawful for the Governor, on good cause shown by the Divisional Council of any of the divisions of the Colony to suspend, by proclamation in the *Gazette*, in whole or in part, as may seem right, the operation of this Act, or any part or parts thereof, in the said division, for any time, or with regard to any animal, or both, for any time and with regard to any animal to be specified in the said proclamation.

13. Any offender being convicted for contravention of any of the provisions of this Act, in default of payment of the fine imposed upon him, and in default of other provision in that behalf in this Act specially provided, shall be liable to imprisonment for any period not exceeding one month, with or without hard labour, unless the fine be sooner paid.

14. In any prosecution for infringement of any section of this Act, by doing anything without licence, it shall be prima facie sufficient for the prosecutor to show that the accused does not appear as the holder of a licence in the list of persons to whom the requisite licence in such case shall have been issued, respectively, kept in the office of the Resident Magistrate before whom or in whose district such case shall be brought for trial in any Court; but it shall be lawful for such accused person to rebut such evidence by proof that he was in fact, at the time of the commission of the offence charged, the lawful holder of such a licence.

15. Until otherwise proclaimed by the Governor, under the provisions of this Act, the fence or close season at present established by law shall continue to be such fence or close season.

16. No landowner shall require a game licence for the purpose of shooting game on his own land.

17. This Act may be cited as the "Game Law Amendment Act, 1886."

Appendix II

September 19, 1893

Proclamation

Whereas it is expedient to regulate the granting of licences, authorising the killing of certain game, in the territory known as the Bechuanaland Protectorate (including the Tati District), and to provide for the payment of certain fees in respect of the granting of such licences:

Now, therefore, under and by virtue of the powers, authorities and jurisdiction conferred upon and committed to me by Her Majesty, I do hereby proclaim, declare and make known as follows:-

1. The operation of this Proclamation is limited to the territories as defined in Section three of my Proclamation of the 27th day of September, 1892.

2. For the purposes of this Proclamation the following term shall have the meaning herein assigned to it, viz.:–

"Large Game" shall mean the Wild Ostrich and the several animals following, not being domesticated, and commonly known as Hippopotamus, Rhinoceros, Buffalo, Zebra, Quagga, and all animals of the Antelope species, except Eland, Duiker and Steinbok.

3. It shall be lawful for the Assistant Commissioner exercising jurisdiction within the territory or territories of any Native Chief or Chiefs to issue with the consent of such Chief or Chiefs as the case may require to any person or number of persons not exceeding five and forming one party, applying there for a licence to shoot large game within the territory or territories of the Chief or Chiefs so consenting as aforesaid. Provided, however, that any such Assistant Commissioner shall be at liberty, if he shall consider it necessary and just to do so, to refuse to issue any such licence on the original application, or to refuse to issue a fresh licence on the expiration of any preceding licence.

4. Such licence shall not be transferable, and shall be in force for twelve months from the date thereof.

5. There shall be paid for and in respect of each licence to the Assistant Commissioner issuing the same, the following sums:

(a) £75 to be collected by means of stamps affixed to the licence and cancelled by such Assistant Commissioner.

(b) £25 for and on behalf of each Chief whose consent is necessary and has been obtained, to the issue of such licence, such Assistant Commissioner shall be responsible to pay over to each Native Chief all sums so received on his behalf.

6. The period from the first day of September in each year to the last day of February in the succeeding year, both inclusive, shall be a close or fence season, within which it shall be unlawful to kill, catch, capture, pursue, hunt or shoot at such game during such close season.

7. No person shall, at any time, with or without any licence or permit, catch, capture, pursue, hunt or shoot at any Elephant, Giraffe or Eland; and every person contravening this section shall be liable upon conviction to a penalty not exceeding £150 (one hundred and fifty pounds sterling), and in default of payment to imprisonment with or without hard labour for any period not exceeding twelve months.

8. Any person who shall, save as hereinafter provided, kill, catch, capture, pursue, hunt or shoot at any large game without having previously obtained a licence or permit under the provisions of this Proclamation, or after the expiration

of the time for which such licence or permit shall have been granted or in violation of the terms thereof or during the close or fence season in section 6 referred to, shall be liable to a penalty not exceeding one hundred and fifty pounds, and in default of payment to imprisonment with or without hard labour for any period not exceeding twelve months.

9. It shall be lawful for any member of the Bechuanaland Border Police or any other person authorised thereto by any Resident Commissioner, Assistant Commissioner or Magistrate, within the limits of his jurisdiction, at any time to demand the production of his licence or permit by any person engaged in the pursuit of large game, and any person failing or refusing to produce the same shall be liable on conviction, to a penalty not exceeding fifty pounds, and in default of payment to imprisonment with or without hard labour for any period not exceeding four months.

10. Any penalties imposed by this Proclamation may be sued for before any Resident Commissioner, Assistant Commissioner or Magistrate having jurisdiction, and all such penalties may be recovered by the seizure and sale of any property belonging to the person so convicted, and any portion of the penalties recovered, not exceeding in any case one-half, shall be paid to the person (not being in the service of the Bechuanualand Government) on whose information the conviction was obtained, and the balance shall be paid into the revenue.

11. Notwithstanding anything to the contrary in this Proclamation contained, it shall be lawful for the Assistant Commissioner from time to time to issue permits, hereinafter styled Station permits, to the Officer Commanding at any places where members of the Bechuanaland Border Police Force and officials in the service of the Government are stationed, authorizing and allowing the members of the said force and the said officials to kill, catch, capture, pursue, hunt, or shoot at a certain quantity of large game, the number and nature of the same to be specified in the said Station permit; such permit shall remain in force for a period of one year from the date of issue, and shall have force and effect throughout all territory within a distance of thirty miles from the place or station in respect of which it shall be issued. It shall be lawful for the Officer Commanding at such station, upon receipt of such Station permit, to grant and issue from time to time, within the said year during which such Station permit shall remain in force, to any member of the said force under his command or to any Government official at such station, a permit under his hand authorizing and allowing such person to kill, catch, capture, pursue, hunt or shoot at a certain number of animals being of the description of large game in the said Station permit mentioned and within the said distance of thirty miles; provided that the total number of animals in respect of which such permits shall be issued shall not exceed the number specified in the said Station permit.

12. Notwithstanding anything to the contrary in this Proclamation contained the following persons may without taking out a licence under this Proclamation kill large game in reasonable quantities for food, except during the close season defined in Art. 6 of this Proclamation:-

(a) All persons in the service of the Government of British Bechuanaland or the Bechuanaland Protectorate when travelling on duty.

(b) Persons travelling on any ordinary roads within a distance of not more than one mile from such road.

13. The permission of this proclamation shall not apply to the members of any Native tribe killing large game or Elephants, Giraffes or Elands within the territory in the occupation of such tribe.

Appendix III

Chronological List of Enactments 1891–1987

Year	Enactment		Purport	Remarks
1891	Act 24 of 1884		Ostrich Export Duty Act.	Repealed P. 39/1907.
	Act 36 of 1886		Game Law Amendment Act.	Repealed P. 17/1925.
1893	Proc.		Hunting licences.	Repealed P. 22/1904.
1904	Proc.	22	Large Game Preservation.	Repealed P. 17/1925.
1906	Proc.	5	Protection of giraffe.	Repealed P. 17/1925.
	Proc.	7	Amendment Proc. 5.	Repealed P. 17/1925.
1907	Proc.	2	Protection of game.	Repealed P. 17/1925.
	Proc.	3	Amendment Proc. 2.	Repealed P. 17/1925.
	Proc.	39	Prohibition of export of ostriches and ostrich eggs.	Repealed A. 7/1966.
	HCN	130	Exemption to ostrich export restrictions.	Repealed A. 7/1966.
1908	HCN	21	Exemption to ostrich export restrictions.	Repealed A. 7/1966.
	HCN	75	Exemption to ostrich export restrictions.	Repealed A. 7/1966.
	HCN	104	Exemption to ostrich export restrictions.	Repealed A. 7/1966.
1909	Proc. 14		Declaration of close season.	Repealed P. 17/1925.
	HCN 58		Exemption to ostrich export restrictions.	Repealed A. 7/1966.
1911	Proc. 1		Amendment P. 14/1909.	Repealed A. 7/1966.
	Proc. 42		Restriction on sale of small game.	Repealed P. 17/1925.
1914	Proc. 44		Plumage Birds Protection and Preservation.	Repealed A. 36/1967.
1922	Proc. 14		Landowner exempt from licence fees.	Repealed P. 17/1925.
	Proc. 29		Protection of rhinoceros.	Repealed P. 17/1925.
1923	Proc. 23		Wildebeest may be excluded from definition Large Game.	Repealed P. 17/1925.
	HCN	90	Wildebeest not protected in Tuli Block.	1 year.
1924	HCN	20	Protection of Large Game on Crown land north of Molopo River.	1 year.
	HCN	71	Renewal HCN 90/1923.	1 year.
1925	Proc.	17	Game Proclamation.	Repealed P. 19/1940.
	HCN	30	Renewal HCN 20/1924.	1 year.
	HCN	104	Renewal HCN 71/1924.	1 year.
1926	HCN	17	Close season, Chobe District.	1 year.

Year	Enactment		Purport	Remarks
	HCN	18	Renewal HCN 30/1925	1 year.
	HCN	76	Renewal HCN 104/1925.	1 year.
1927	HCN	8	Renewal HCN 18/1926.	1 year.
	HCN	64	Renewal HCN 76/1926.	1 year.
1928	HCN	85	Renewal HCN 64/1927.	1 year.
1929	Proc.	48	Burden of proof for possession of game products.	Repealed P. 19/1940.
	HCN	4	Renewal HCN 8/1927.	1 year.
	HCN	23	Game protected on unalienated land Tuli Block.	1 year.
	HCN	63	Renewal HCN 85/1928.	1 year.
	HCN	75	Close season: Chobe and Ngamiland Districts.	1 year.
1930	Proc.	27	Forfeiture of firearms and ammunition.	Repealed P. 27/1930.
	HCN	10	Wildbeest not protected in Tuli Block, Ngwato and Francistown Districts.	Revoked HCN 128/1930
	HCN	12	Protection of certain large birds as Large Game.	Repealed P. 19/1940.
	HCN	27	Renewal HCN 4/1929.	1 year.
	HCN	128	Cancellation HCN 10/1930.	
1931	HCN	33	Renewal HCN 27/1930 extended to Small Game.	1 year.
1932	Proc.	12	Amendment licence fees.	Repealed P. 19/1940
	HCN	53	Protection of game in Chobe District.	3 years.
1933	Proc.	53	Wild Birds Protection and Preservation.	Repealed A. 36/1967.
	HCN	139	Renewal HCN 53/1932 with area extension.	3 years.
1935	HCN	17	Renewal HCN 139/1933	3 years.
	HCN	166	Kudu not protected in Francistown District.	Repealed P. 19/1940.
	HCN	167	Wildebeest not protected in Tuli Block.	Cancelled by HCN 145/1938.
1936	HCN	52	Renewal HCN 33/1931.	1 year.
1937	HCN	61	Renewal HCN 52/1936.	1 year.
	HCN	177	Protection of Large Game in part Ngamiland District.	1 year.
1938	Proc.	7	Amendment sec. 11 P. 17/1925.	Repealed P. 19/1940.
	HCN	33	Renewal HCN 17/1935.	3 years.
	HCN	41	Renewal HCN 61/1937.	1 year.
	HCN	44	Protection game birds at Mogobane Dam.	3 years.
	HCN	145	Cancellation HCN 167/1935.	

Year	Enactment	Purport	Remarks
1939	HCN 33	Renewal HCN 41/1938.	1 year.
	HCN 64	Removal of protection of game in part of Ngamiland District.	1 year.
	HCN 121	Wildebeest not protected in Bakgatla Reserve.	Revoked by SI 106/1973.
1940	Proc. 19	Game Proclamation.	Amended P. 25/1944; P. 4/1945; P. 2/1948; P. 54/1948; P. 41/1949; replaced by cap. 114/1950.
	HCN 42	Renewal HCN 33/1939 with Districts specified.	1 year.
	HCN 105	Hippopotamus classed as Large Game.	Incoporated cap. 114/1950.
	HCN 106	Protection of game in Chobe, Ghanzi and Kgalagadi Districts being repeats of HCN 33/1938 and 42/1940.	1 year.
	HCN 107	Declaration of Nosop River Game Reserve.	
	HCN 108	Declaration of Mogobane Dam bird Sanctuary.	Repealed by HCN 115/1947.
	HCN 229	Ports of Exit for game products.	Amended by HCN 37/1943.
1941	HCN 39	Renewal HCN 42/1940.	1 year.
	HCN 42	Protection of certain birds in Bakgatla Reserve.	3 years.
	HCN 189	Changes in protection of springbok and wildebeest in certain areas.	Amended by HCN 189/1941 and 117/1952.
	HCN 200	Renewal HCN 106/1940	1 year.
1942	HCN 37	Amendment HCN 189/1941 in respect of wildebeest.	
	HCN 46	Renewal HCN 39/1941.	1 year.
	HCN 196	Changes in protection of certain species in certain areas.	Amended by HCN 117/1952.
	HCN 274	Declaration of Bathoen Dam bird Sanctuary.	Amended HCN 115/1947; 116/1947; cap. 38 : 01/1976.
	HCN 306	Renewal HCN 200/1941.	1 year.
1943	HCN 37	Ports of Exit.	Repealed P. 22/1961.
	HCN 50	Removal of protection of game along Maun-Kasane road.	Cancelled by HCN 65/1960.
1944	Proc. 25	Amended P. 19/1940. including permitting destruction of game causing damage.	Repealed cap. 114/1950.

Year	Enactment	Purport	Remarks
	HCN 26	Protection of springbok in Lobatse District.	Replaced by HCN 193/1946.
	HCN 44	Renewal HCN 46/1942.	1 year.
	HCN 90	Renewal HCN 42/1941.	3 years.
1945	Proc. 4	Amending P. 19/1940.	Repealed P. 22/1961.
	HCN 71	Renewal HCN 44/1944.	1 year.
1946	HCN 123	Renewal HCN 71/1945.	Cancelled by HCN 265/1946.
	HCN 193	Protection of game in Lobatse District.	1 year.
	HCN 265	Replaced HCN 123/1946.	1 year.
1947	Proc. 66	Amendment to P. 19/1940.	Repealed P. 22/1961.
	HCN 115	Removal of protection for certain game birds in Mogobane and Bathoen Dam Sanctuaries.	
	HCN 116	Removal of protection for certain birds in Mogobane and Bathoen Dam Sanctuaries.	Amended by cap. 38:01/1976.
	HCN 125	Renewal HCN 265/1946	1 year.
1948	Law cap. 144	Game Proclamation	Repealed P. 22/1961.
	Proc. 2	Amendment licence fees, P. 19/1940.	Repealed P. 22/1961.
	Proc. 58	Amendment P. 19/1940, native hunting.	Repealed P. 22/1961.
	HCN 86	Protection of species in Tuli Block.	3 years.
	HCN 143	Renewal HCN 125/1947.	1 year.
	HCN 196	Renewal HCN 193/1946.	3 years.
	HCN 262	Declaration of Sanctuary in Fort Tuli area.	Repealed HCN 182/1951.
1949	Proc. 41	Amendment P. 19/1940.	Repealed P. 22/1961.
	HCN 157	Renewal HCN 143/1948.	1 year.
1950	HCN 180	Renewal HCN 157/1949	3 years.
	HCN 228	Laws of Bechuanaland.	Introduced cap. 114.
1951	HCN 182	Cancelled HCN 262/1948.	
1952	Proc. 3	Amendments to cap. 114.	Repealed P. 22/1961.
	HCN 54	Close season in Batawana Reserve.	1 year.
	HCN 57	Renewal HCN 196/1948 and 180/1950.	3 years.
	HCN 117	Protection of springbok.	Replaced P. 22/1961.
1953	Proc. 11	Amendment cap. 114.	Repealed P. 22/1961.
	Proc. 39	Amendment cap. 114.	Repealed P. 22/1961.
	HCN 69	Close season Batawana Reserve.	2 years.

Year	Enactment		Purport	Remarks
	HCN	70	Protection removed from wildebeest.	Replaced P. 22/1961.
1954	HCN	3	Export duty on skins and hippopotamus hide.	Replaced P. 22/1961.
	HCN	24	Exclusion of red-billed weaver bird from protection under cap. 115.	
1955	GN	32	Close season Batawana Reserve.	1 year.
	HCN	203	Renewal HCN 57/1952.	3 years.
1956	GN	20	Close season Batawana Reserve.	1 year.
1959	HCN	65	Renewal HCN 203/1955.	3 years.
1960	HCN	65	Establishment of Chobe Game . Reserve.	Amended GN 86/1964; revoked SI 125/1980.
1961	Proc.	22	Fauna Conservation Proclamation.	Replaced by cap. 38:01/1976.
	HCN	33	Establishment of Central Kalahari Game Reserve.	
	GN	49	Open season for hunting.	Cancelled GN 28/1962.
	GN	52	Licence formats.	Amended SI 36/1967; 2/1968;19/1968; replaced cap. 38:01/1976
1962	Law	16	Amendment P. 22/1961.	Replaced cap. 38:01/1976
	Law	38	Amendment P. 22/1961, duty on wildebeest skins.	Replaced cap. 38:01/1976
	GN	27	Amendment P. 22/1961.	Replaced cap. 38:01/1976
	GN	28	Open season for hunting.	Cancelled GN 22/1963
1963	GN	22	Open season for hunting.	Cancelled GN 155/1964
	GN	38	Central Kalahari Game Reserve. (control of entry) Regulations.	
	GN	49	Chobe Game Reserve Regulations.	Amended GN 85/1964; SI 81/1968 (fees); revoked SI 37/1987.
1964	Law	4	Amendments P. 22/1961.	Replaced cap. 38:01/1976
	Law	39	Amendments P.22/1961.	Replaced cap. 38:01/1976
	GN	38	Commutation of export duty.	Repealed LN 20/1965.
	GN	57	Revision licence fees.	Replaced cap. 38:01/1976.
	GN	85	Amendment GN 49/1963.	Revoked SI 37/1987.
	GN	86	Alteration of limits of Chobe Game Reserve.	Replaced cap. 38:01/ 1976.
	GN	87	Commencement Chobe Game Reserve Regulations.	Revoked SI 37/1987.
	GN	137	Moremi Wildlife Reserve Regulations.	Amended SI 67/1973; revoked SI 102/1979.
	GN	155	Open season for hunting.	Cancelled LN 26/1965
1965	Law	4	Amendment P. 22/1961, package licences.	Replaced cap. 38:01/1976.
	LN	14	Declaration Moremi Wildlife Reserve.	Replaced cap. 38:01/1976; amended SI 93/1976.
	LN	20	Licensing regulations.	Cancelled SI 19/1968.

Year	Enactment		Purport	Remarks
	LN	26	Open season for hunting.	Cancelled SI 40/1967.
	LN	32	Commencement Moremi Wildlife Reserve Regulations.	Revoked SI 111/1979.
	LN	33	Amendment LN 32/1965.	Revoked SI 102/1979.
	GN	22	Open season for hunting.	Cancelled LN 26/1965.
1966	Act	7	Ostrich Export (Repeal).	Repeal cap. 160.
	Law	42	Amendments P. 22/1961.	Replaced cap. 38:01/1976.
	LN	98	Additions to Royal Game Schedule.	Replaced A. 47/1967.
1967	Act	36	Repeal Wild Birds Protection Proclamation.	
	Act	47	Amendments P. 22/1961.	Replaced cap. 38 :01/1976.
	Act	48	National Parks Act	
	SI	25	State land hunting regulations.	Amended SI 39/1967.
	SI	30	Records and returns by trophy dealers regulations.	Revoked SI 76/1967.
	SI	36	Amendment to licence formats.	Cancelled SI 19/1968.
	SI	37	Powers of honorary officers.	Cancelled SI 19/1968.
	SI	39	Amendment SI 25/1967.	
	SI	40	Open season for hunting.	Cancelled SI 8/1969.
	SI	49	Amendment P. 22/1961, ivory and rhinoceros horn registration.	Cancelled SI 19/1968.
	SI	64	Bamangwato Tribal Territory Hunting Regulations.	Amended SI 32/1970; 82/1970; 44/1971; 71/1976; revoked SI 19/ 1979.
	SI	65	Batawana Tribal Territory Hunting Regulations.	Amended SI 6/1969; 33/1970; 43/1971; 39/1975; 72/1976; revoked SI 19/1979.
	SI	74	Names of animals.	
	SI	76	Trophy dealers' Regulations.	Revoked SI 81/1971.
	GN	17	Declaration of Private Game Reserve.	
	GN	48	Authorisation of Game officers and Game Scouts.	Replaced A. 1/1979.
	GN	76	Appointment of Honorary Officer.	3 years.
	GN	96	Authorisation of Game Officer, appointment of authorised officers.	Replaced A. 1/1979.
	GN	102	Declaration of Private Game Reserves.	
	GN	103	Appointment of Honorary Officer.	3 years.

Year	Enactment		Purport	Remarks
1968	SI	2	Amendment GN 52/1961 licence formats.	Replaced cap. 38: 01/1976
	SI	3	Capture fees.	Amended SI 51/1973.
	SI	4	Declaration Controlled Hunting Areas (Bakwena Tribal Territory).	Amended SI 12/1970.
	SI	7	Kweneng Controlled Hunting Areas Regulations.	Amended SI 5/1969; 22/1970; revoked SI 27/1971.
	SI	9	Klipspringer removed from Protected Game Schedule.	Replaced cap. 38:01/1976
	SI	13	Amendment Batawana Tribal Territory Hunting Regulations.	Revoked SI 19/1979.
	SI	15	Declaration of controlled Hunting Areas on State land	Amended SI 83/1973; 5/1975; revoked 93/1977
	SI	16	Amendment of schedules, Fauna Proclamation.	Replaced cap. 38: 01/1976
	SI	17	State land Controlled Hunting Areas Regulations.	Amended SI 4/1968; 37/1969; 31/1970; 30/1971; 92/1977; revoked SI 19/1979.
	SI	19	Amendments to licensing regulations.	Amended SI 86/1968; 9/1969; 48/1969; 28/1971; 31/1974; revoked SI 111/1980.
	SI	21	Amendment to export duty.	Replaced cap. 38:01/1976
	SI	22	Declaration of Controlled Hunting Areas in Tribal Territories.	
	SI	23	Regulations for Controlled Hunting Areas in Tribal Territories.	Amended SI 7/1969; 38/1969; 21/1970; 42/1970; 32/1971; 58/1971; revoked SI 19/1979.
	SI	27	Declaration of Lake Ngami Controlled Hunting Area.	
	SI	28	Lake Ngami Controlled Hunting Area Regulations.	Revoked SI 19/1979.
	SI	35	Payees of Controlled Hunting Area fees.	
	SI	37	Bakwena Tribal Territory hunting regulations.	Amended SI 94/1970; 86/1972; 67/1974; revoked SI 19/1979; 'A' revoked by SI 84/1979.
	SI	55	Declaration of Private Game Reserves.	
	SI	56	Bangwaketse Tribal Territory hunting regulations.	Amended SI 71/1971; 85/1972; 40/1975; 57/1976; revoked SI 19/1979.

Year	Enactment		Purport	Remarks
	SI	76	Declaration of Private Game Reserve.	
	SI	81	Chobe National Park fees revision.	Amended SI 54/1976.
	SI	86	Amendments to forms.	Revoked SI 111/1980.
	SI	87	Declaration of Private Game Reserve.	
	GN	48	Appointment of authorised officers.	Amended GN 256/1969; replaced A. 1/1979.
	GN	56	Appointment of licensing officers.	
	GN	63	Fauna Conservation (Amendment) Act, 1967, date of commencement.	Replaced A. 1/1979.
	GN	64	National Parks Act, 1967, date of commencement.	
	GN	65	The Wild Birds Protection (Repeal) Act, 1967, date of commencement.	
	GN	67	Hunting quotas	1 year.
	GN	102	Declaration of Controlled Hunting Area residents.	
	GN	126	Licensing officer stations.	
	GN	127	Licensing officer stations.	
	GN	347	Declaration of Controlled Hunting Area residents.	
1969	SI	3	Declaration of Private Game reserve.	
	SI	4	Amendment State land Controlled Hunting Area regulations.	Corrected GN 27/1969; revoked SI 19/1979.
	SI	5	Amendment Kweneng Controlled Hunting Areas regulations.	Revoked SI 19/1979.
	SI	6	Amendment Batawana Tribal Territory hunting regulations.	Revoked SI 19/1979.
	SI	7	Amendment Tribal Territories Controlled Hunting Areas regulations.	Revoked SI 19/1979.
	SI	8	Open hunting seasons.	Revoked SI 11/1973.
	SI	9	Amendment to general regulations.	Revoked SI 111/1980.
	SI	16	Amendment schedules Fauna Conservation Proclamation, including animals which may not be	Incorporated cap. 38:01/1976.

Year	Enactment		Purport	Remarks
			hunted on landholder's privileges.	
	SI	17	Amendment to export duty.	Incorporated cap. 38:01/1976.
	SI	37	Amendment State land Controlled Hunting Area regulations.	Revoked SI 19/1979.
	SI	38	Amendment Tribal Territories Controlled Hunting Area regulations.	Revoked SI 19/1979.
	SI	42	Amendment to export duty.	Incorporated cap. 38:01/1976.
	SI	48	Amendment licence format.	Revoked SI 111/1980.
	SI	58	Declaration Maun Game Sanctuary.	
	SI	116	Fees for certain species.	Revoked SI 29/1971.
	SI	122	Declaration Nuane Dam Game Reserve.	
	GN	7	Appointment licensing officers.	
	GN	27	Correction State land Controlled Hunting Areas regulations.	Revoked SI 19/1979.
	GN	252	Appointment licensing officers.	
	GN	253	Appointment Chief Game Warden.	Replaced by GN 208/1974.
	GN	254	Appointment Director of National Parks.	
	GN	256	Appointment authorised officers.	Revoked A. 1/1979.
	GN	493	Appointment honorary officers.	3 years.
1970	Act	64	Amendment forfeiture provisions.	Amended A. 1/1979.
	SI	9	Amendment export duty.	Incorporated cap. 38:01/1976.
	SI	12	Amendment Kweneng Controlled Hunting Area names.	
	SI	20	Amendment licence fees.	Incorporated cap. 38:01/1976.
	SI	21	Amendment Tribal Territories Controlled Hunting Areas regulations.	Revoked SI 19/1979.
	SI	22	Amendment Kweneng Controlled Hunting Areas regulations.	Revoked SI 27/1971.

Year	Enactment		Purport	Remarks
	SI	31	Amendment State land Controlled Hunting Areas regulations.	Revoked SI 19/1979.
	SI	32	Amendment Bamangwato Tribal Territory Hunting regulations.	Revoked SI 19/1979.
	SI	33	Amendment Batawana Tribal Territory Hunting Regulations.	Revoked SI 19/1979.
	SI	41	Declaration Tribal Territory Controlled Hunting Area.	
	SI	42	Amendment Tribal Territories Controlled Hunting Area Regulations.	Revoked SI 19/1979.
	SI	43	Declaration Tribal Territories Controlled Hunting Areas.	
	SI	44	Declaration Private Game Reserves.	
	SI	82	Amendment Bamangwato Tribal Territory Hunting Regulations.	Revoked SI 19/1979.
	SI	83	Declaration Makgadikgadi Pans Game Reserve.	
	SI	94	Amendment Bakwena Tribal Territory Hunting Regulations	Revoked SI 19/1979.
	GN	67	Controlled Hunting Area quotas.	1 year.
	GN	76	Controlled Hunting Area quotas.	1 year.
	GN	77	Controlled Hunting Area quotas.	1 year.
	GN	273	Proposed constitution of Nxai Pan National Park.	Declared SI 59/1970.
1971	SI	10	Declaration Mabuasehube Game Reserve.	Amended SI 10/1987.
	SI	19	Declaration Private Game Reserves.	
	SI	27	Revocation Kweneng Controlled Hunting Areas regulations	
	SI	28	Amendment licensing regulations.	Revoked SI 111/1980.
	SI	29	Amendment permit fees.	Amended SI 33/1974.
	SI	30	Amendment State land Controlled Hunting Area fees.	Replaced SI 19/1979.
	SI	31	Amendment Fauna Conservation Proclamation schedules.	Incorporated cap. 38: 01/1976.
	SI	32	Amendment Tribal	Revoked SI 19/1979.

100

Year	Enactment		Purport	Remarks
			Territories Controlled Hunting Areas regulations.	
	SI	37	Amendment Fauna Conservation Proclamation schedule.	Incorporated cap. 38: 01/1976.
	SI	43	Amendment Batawana Tribal Territory Hunting Regulations	Amended SI 46/1973; revoked SI 19/1979.
	SI	44	Amendment Bamangwato Tribal Territory Hunting Regulations.	revoked SI 19/1979.
	SI	48	Declaration Private Game Reserves.	
	SI	53	Declaration Tribal Territory Controlled Hunting Area.	
	SI	58	Amendment Tribal Territories Controlled Hunting Regulations.	Revoked SI 19/1979.
	SI	59	Declaration Nxai Pan National Park.	
	SI	71	Amendment Bangwaketse Tribal Territory Hunting Regulations.	Revoked SI 19/1979.
	SI	78	Declaration Khutse Game Reserve.	
	SI	81	Trophy dealers' Regulations	Amended SI 111/1980.
	SI	83	Declaration Gemsbok National Park.	Amended SI 9/1987.
	SI	94	Chobe National Park, Kachikau-Kasane road traffic regulations.	
1972	SI	85	Amendment Bangwaketse Tribal Territory Hunting Regulations.	Revoked SI 19/1979.
	SI	86	Amendment Bakwena Tribal Territory Hunting Regulations.	Revoked SI 19/1979.
	GN	83	Authorised officers.	Revoked A. 1/1979.
	GN	162	Appointment honorary officers.	3 years.
	GN	338	Cancellation of trophy dealers' licenses	
1973	SI	11	Amendment to open season.	Revoked SI 68/1974.
	SI	46	Amendment Batawana Tribal Territory Hunting Regulations.	Revoked SI 19/1979.
	SI	51	Amendment capture fees.	
	SI	59	Declaration Private Game Reserves.	
	SI	67	Amendment Moremi Wildlife Reserve entrance fees.	Revoked SI 102/1979.

Year	Enactment		Purport	Remarks
	SI	83	Amendment Controlled Hunting Area No. 10.	
	SI	106	Bakgatla Tribal Territory Hunting Regulations.	Revoked SI 19/1979.
1974	SI	31	Amendment General Regulations, 1968.	Revoked SI 111/1980.
	SI	32	Amentment Fauna Conservation Proclamation schedules.	Incorporated cap. 38: 01/1976.
	SI	33	Amendment permit fees.	
	SI	41	Authorised officers.	Revoked A. 1/1979.
	SI	67	Amendment Bakwena Tribal Territory Hunting Regulations.	Revoked SI 19/1979.
	SI	68	Declaration open season.	Revoked SI 33/1975.
	SI	85	Driver/courier Regulations.	
	SI	107	Declaration Private Game Reserve.	Revoked SI 84/1979.
	SI	145	Declaration Maikaelelo Game Reserve.	Incorporated cap. 38: 01 /1976; revoked SI 125/ 1980.
	SI	153	Declaration Private Game Reserves.	
	GN	208	Appointment Chief Game Warden.	Replaced 1979.
	GN	293	Controlled Hunting Area quotas.	1 year.
	GN	294	Controlled Hunting Area quotas.	1 year.
	GN	295	Controlled Hunting Area quotas.	1 year.
	GN	427	Proposed extensions to Chobe National Park.	Incorporated cap. 38: 03/ 1976.
1975	SI	5	Amendment State land Controlled Hunting Area.	
	SI	33	Declaration open season.	Revoked SI 59/1976.
	SI	39	Amendment Batawana Tribal Territory hunting fees.	Revoked SI 19/1979.
	SI	40	Amendment Bangwaketse Tribal Territory Hunting Re-gulations.	Revoked SI 19/1979.
	SI	67	Amendment export duty.	Replaced cap. 38: 01/1976
	SI	141	Declaration Gaborone Dam National Park.	Revoked SI 55/1979.
	GN	107	Controlled Hunting Area quotas.	1 year.
	GN	108	Controlled Hunting Area quotas.	1 year.
	GN	109	Controlled Hunting Area quotas.	1 year.

Year	Enactment		Purport	Remarks
1976	Act cap. 38 : 01		Fauna Conservation Act.	Introduced by the Law Revision Order SI 160/1976; amended A. 1/1979.
	Act cap. 38 : 03		National Parks Act.	Introduced by the Law Revision Order SI 160/1976; amended SI 126/1980.
	SI	54	Chobe National Park fees.	Replaced SI 37/1987.
	SI	57	Amendment Bangwaketse Tribal Territory Hunting Regulations.	Revoked SI 19/1979.
	SI	58	Amendment Fauna Conservation Act schedule.	Incorporated cap. 38 : 01/1976.
	SI	59	Declaration open season.	Revoked SI 27/1977.
	SI	67	Amendment export duty.	Incorporated cap. 38 : 01/1976.
	SI	71	Amendment Bamangwato Tribal Territory Hunting Regulations.	Revoked SI 19/1979.
	SI	72	Amendment Batawana Tribal Territory Hunting Regulations.	Revoked SI 19/1979.
	SI	93	Amendment Moremi Wildlife Reserve boundaries.	Incorporated cap. 38 : 01/1976.
	SI	127	Khutse Game Reserve Regulations.	
	SI	128	Nxai Pan National Park Regulations.	
	GN	52	Controlled Hunting Area quotas.	1 year.
	GN	53	Controlled Hunting Area quotas.	1 year.
	GN	54	Controlled Hunting Area quotas	1 year
1977	SI	27	Declaration open season.	Replaced SI 30/1980.
	SI	35	Khutse Game Reserve Regulations commencement.	
	SI	36	Nxai Pan National Park Regulations commencement.	
	SI	92	Amendment State land Controlled Hunting Area Regulations.	Revoked SI 19/1979.
	SI	93	Declaration Controlled Hunting Areas.	
	GN	184	Controlled Hunting Areas quotas.	1 year.
	GN	185	Controlled Hunting Areas quotas.	1 year.

Year	Enactment		Purport	Remarks
	GN	186	Controlled Hunting Areas quotas.	1 year.
1978	SI	97	Declaration Controlled Hunting Area.	
	GN	154	Controlled Hunting Areas quotas.	1 year.
	GN	155	Controlled Hunting Areas quotas.	1 year.
	GN	156	Controlled Hunting Areas quotas.	1 year.
1979	Act	1	Fauna Conservation (Amendment) Act.	Replaced cap. 38:01, LRO 1/1982.
	SI	18	Fauna Conservation (Amendment) Act commencement.	Replaced cap. 38: 01, LRO 1/1982.
	SI	19	Fauna Conservation (Unified Hunting) Regulations.	Amended SI 31/1979.
	SI	31	Amendment Unified Hunting Regulations.	
	SI	55	Revocation Gaborone Dam National Park.	
	SI	84	Revocation Private Game Reserves.	SI 107/1974.
	SI	102	Moremi Game Reserve Regulations.	
	SI	111	Moremi Game Reserve Regulations commencement.	
	GN	188	Controlled Hunting Area quotas.	1 year.
	GN	198	Proposal that Gaborone Dam National Park cease to be a national park.	Confirmed SI 55/1979.
	GN	206	Controlled Hunting Area quotas.	1 year.
	GN	337	Declaration Gaborone Game Reserve.	Confirmed SI 138/1980.
1980	SI	30	Declaration open season.	Revoked SI 37/1986.
	SI	111	General Regulations.	
	SI	125	Revocation Chobe and Maikaelelo Game Reserves.	
	SI	126	Amendment Chobe National Park boundary.	Replaced SI 9/1987.
	SI	135	Compensation for destruction livestock and other property.	Amended SI 16/1981.
	SI	138	Declaration Gaborone Dam Game Reserve.	

Year	Enactment	Purport	Remarks
	GN 169	Controlled Hunting Areas quotas.	1 year.
1981	SI 16	Compensation for destruction livestock and other property.	
	GN 116	Controlled Hunting Area quotas.	1 year.
1982	Act cap. 38:01	Fauna Conservation Act.	Incorporation amendments; amended SI 72/1982.
	SI 38	Powers Honorary Game Officers.	
	SI 72	Amendment Fauna Conservation Act.	
	GN 134	Controlled Hunting Area quotas.	1 year.
1983	GN 192	Controlled Hunting Area quotas.	1 year.
1984	GN 273	Controlled Hunting Area quotas	1 year.
1985	SI 26	Declaration Jwaneng Controlled Hunting Areas.	
	SI 27	Declaration Private Game Reserve.	
	SI 28	Declaration Private Game Reserve.	
	SI 89	Declaration Mannyelanong Game Reserve.	
	SI 90	Mannyelanong Game Reserve Regulations.	
	GN 100	Controlled Hunting Area quotas.	1 year.
1986	SI 37	Declaration open season.	
	GN 144	Controlled Hunting Area quotas.	1 year.
1987	SI 9	National Parks Constitution.	
	SI 10	Amendment Fauna Conservation Act Game Reserves and Sanctuaries schedule.	
	SI 37	Chobe National Park Regulations.	
	GN 81	Controlled Hunting Areas quotas.	1 year.

A. = Act; P. = Proclamation; Proc. = Proclamation; HCN = High Commissioner's Notice; SI = Statutory Instrument; GN = Government Notice; LN = Legal Notice; LRO = Law Revision Order.

Appendix IV

GAME : FUTURE POLICY

[October 1961]

A policy of game preservation has been followed throughout the Territory for many years and partly as a result of this and partly owing to the low density of human population the Bechuanaland Protectorate is one of the few remaining areas in Africa where large numbers and varieties of game are to be found. The hunting of game in European farming areas and on Crown Lands has always been rigidly controlled under licence and in the Tribal Territories African Authorities have imposed limited restrictions on Tribal hunting. It is not therefore surprising that game is still to be found in all but the smallest Tribal Territories and that the European farming areas, with the exception of the Lobatsi Block, still carry a large game population.

2. The new Fauna Conservation Proclamation which was promulgated in 1960, and which applies to hunting by Africans on Crown Lands, hunting by licensed European hunters, and to hunting by landholders in farming areas, has to some extent altered the traditional policy as regards the hunting of game in these areas, and the present position is as follows:

(a) Hunting by Africans on Crown Lands.

Africans may be authorised to shoot all game except Royal Game without restriction, or even the latter under Resident Commissioner's Licence, they may be authorised to shoot limited numbers or restricted species of game or they may be prohibited from hunting altogether. Regulations under this section of the law have not as yet been published and for the present the status quo has been maintained. Thus in the Kgalagadi district, for instance, the African residents are permitted to hunt only certain species of the smaller type of animal.

(b) Hunting by Licensed European Hunters.

Hunting is still rigidly controlled under licence, and fees have been substantially increased to the level of those imposed elsewhere in Africa, but at the same time the list of animals which may be hunted has been substantially increased, it being considered that a licence holder should be permitted to hunt the animals for which he is prepared to pay. Nevertheless, apart from private land in farming areas in respect of which licences may be granted with the consent of the landowners, the only areas which are regularly opened to European hunters are Ngamiland and a small area of Crown Lands north of Nata. Hunting by residents is permitted on a very restricted basis in Tribal Territories such as the Bangwaketse, Bakwena and Bamangwato.

(c) Hunting by Landowners and Occupiers of Land.

Landowners and certain specified occupiers of land have been granted landholders' privileges, in terms of which they may hunt all game, except those species on a short list, throughout the year without licence and in unlimited numbers. They may, on the other hand, ask that their land should be declared a private game reserve for the preservation of game.

3. To complete the picture in so far as present policy regarding the control of hunting in the Territory is concerned it is necessary to consider the hunting of game by the Africans in the Tribal Territories, to which the new Fauna Conservation Proclamation does not apply. African Authorities are empowered in terms of the

African Administration Proclamation to make regulations regarding hunting by residents in their areas. Generally speaking few restrictions are in fact imposed and these generally relate to certain types of Royal Game. In Ngamiland, for instance, no African may shoot an elephant without the permission of the Regent. The imposition of licence fees for African hunters was at one time considered but as far as is known no fees have in fact been levied. Natural increase, the isolation of many parts of the Territory, the relative scarcity of modern firearms, and the fact that the majority of the Africans hunt only for the pot and without wastage, accounts for the large game population which still exists, in many of these areas. There is at present some pressure on Government to revise the annual quotas for arms and ammunition, particularly in regard to Africans. If it was agreed that these quotas should be increased there is no doubt that a greater number of animals would be killed in Tribal Territories, although as skins have a low market value killing would still be confined mainly to hunting for the pot.

4. The three main functions of the Game Department under present policy are to control game where this is necessary in farming areas, to assist hunters and safari companies generally and where necessary to organise hunting expeditions, and to administer the Chobe Game Reserve. The need to control game, particularly elephant over a long period in the Tuli Block has led to a review of the game policy in that area and it has become evident that the development of ranching and agriculture, and the need to introduce more effective disease control measures, makes it inevitable that future policy in the Tuli Block should aim at the destruction of elephant, and the rigid control of other species, as it has been found that the game presents a constant menace to crops and improvements and is generally accepted as being a contributing factor in the spread of foot and mouth disease.

5. The problems of the Tuli Block have helped to draw attention to the fact that a territorial review of the Game policy, especially in relation to the livestock industry should now be undertaken. It is proposed to examine first the future policy of the Game Department which, because of its small size, can concern itself only with the more obvious and immediate aspects of game control, in order to see whether this can be reconciled with a territorial policy attuned to the needs of the livestock industry, and to a lesser extent of agriculture.

6. Game is now regarded in many parts of Africa as a commodity which can be sold or made use of advantageously in one form or another. Provided that provision is made, in areas where there are no other overriding requirements, for the preservation of wild life, often described nowadays as a heritage to be held in trust for future generations, a grant-aided territory such as the Bechuanaland Protectorate can no longer afford to maintain a game department which is not financially self-sufficient or does not contribute to a major industry, such as the livestock industry. In fact, departmental estimates for 1961/62 are very nearly self-balancing in that expenditure of R23,456 is balanced by revenue in respect of export tax on game products, licences and the sale of ivory, amounting to R22,000. Although a certain amount of work has been done to control game movements in farming areas, the need for this would itself have been unnecessary if the game had been destroyed or drastically reduced in these areas rather than preserved.

7. The policy of the Game department will in future be to ensure the preservation of game in the game reserves, particularly in the Chobe Game Reserve which it is hoped will eventually become a self-supporting unit when it has been developed,

and to operate or to assist profitable hunting schemes and safari ventures. The Chobe Reserve is intended to serve the same purposes as for example the Kruger National Park and will require close control by the department. (A Colonial Development and Welfare Scheme has been submitted for the initial development of this reserve.) The new reserve in the Central Kalahari is primarily intended to preserve the flora and fauna which provide the habitat of the "wild "Bushmen; the interest of the Game Department will be more indirect. Nevertheless these reserves, together with the area adjoining the Gemsbok Game Reserve in Gordonia, provide wild life sanctuaries totalling 28,000 square miles, as compared with approximately the same area in the Federation of Rhodesia and Nyasaland, 13,000 square miles in the Republic of South Africa and 33,000 in South West Africa. (The Chobe Game Reserve alone is about 6,000 square miles, as compared with the Kruger National Park, 8,000 sq. miles). It will be seen therefore that the present proposals for control of game in the territory in the interests of its inhabitants are not incompatible with the preservation of wild life on a scale fully matching what has been done in neighbouring countries. As will be explained more fully below, the Game Department can no longer assist in the preservation of game throughout the Territory, because this involves costly patrol and control measures, and because preservation can itself only be justified where it presents no threat to the livestock industry or to agriculture and where it can be seen and enjoyed by all.

8. Any consideration of future game policy in relation to the livestock industry should take into account the three main systems of land tenure that have a direct bearing on the development and economy of the areas concerned. These are Tribal Territories, Crown Lands and European farming blocks. It is proposed to deal with these areas separately.

European Farming Blocks.

9. As has been stated, the new Fauna Conservation Proclamation authorises land-owners to shoot out all the game on their farms, apart from those species on a short list, or to preserve it. It has been agreed that costly game and Police patrols can no longer be maintained purely so as to enable a few wealthy landholders to preserve game, not for the public benefit, but for their own pleasure, and consequently any persons wishing to maintain a private game reserve must do so entirely at his own expense and must ensure that game preserved on his farm does not endanger the crops and farm improvements of his neighbours. In these circumstances, because private game reserves are of no public benefit, and cannot by reason of their limitations contribute materially towards game preservation, and because moreover they constitute a permanent threat to disease control and to the economy of the neighbouring farms, their establishment will be strongly discouraged. It will be for consideration whether their establishment should be prohibited. It may be necessary to go even further by encouraging or even requiring farmers either to destroy *all* game on their farms or to institute very rigid control measures. It would in all probability be necessary for the Game Department itself to undertake the destruction of elephant in farming areas as this is an operation requiring much skill and experience; moreover without concerted action there is a grave risk of the herds being scattered over a wide area, thus prolonging the task unnecessarily. When a number of elephant were destroyed by the Game Department in the Tuli Block a few years ago only five out of the first sixty which were shot did not carry old wounds. The young elephant could be sold at a profit.

Tribal Territories.

10. The problem in Tribal Territories is much more difficult. Apart from the threat to disease control which is ever-present game does not constitute the same threat to farming activities because improvements are few and game in any case for the most part inhabits isolated, waterless areas where cattle can only make use of the grazing if there are pans and for as long as these hold water. Some parts of the Western Bangwaketse and Bakwena provide good examples. Moreover, game is a popular and cheap source of food for the African population, particularly useful in bad years. The importance of this source of protein should not be overlooked. The relatively low incidence of nutrition deficiency diseases in the Bechuanaland Protectorate compared with e.g. Basutoland is at least partly due to this food supply, which in this arid country could only very gradually be replaced by better agriculture.

11. To some residents of these areas, who are often sceptical about the part played by game in the spread of Foot and Mouth Disease, and who regard game not as a threat to other farming activities but as a welcome source of food, and moreover as part of the traditional scene, there would appear to be no great merit in drastically reducing the existing game population. It is, however, becoming increasingly apparent that serious consideration must soon be given to the matter, because the four disease control fences which run through Kuki, Makalamabedi, Dukwe and Lephephe, and which are designed to control cattle movements, are unable alone to control game movements, which are in fact the cause of heavy recurrent maintenance charges. Game could theoretically traverse the territory from North to South and from East to West. The erection of fences capable of controlling game movements other than in Game Reserves would be quite impracticable and the only ultimate solution therefore may be the destruction or drastic reduction of the whole game population.

12. The question of proximity of the Chobe Game Reserve to the Bushman Pits cattle holding area has been raised. In fact the distance between the southern boundary of the former and the northern boundary of the latter is approximately 30 miles and provided steps are taken to keep game away from the immediate neighbourhood of the Bushman Pits fence, there should be no serious risk. If it should prove practicable to fence the southern boundary of the game reserve this will of course be an added safeguard.

13. It is not however suggested that the game population in Tribal Territories should be completely eradicated, even if this were possible; its value as a source of food as already pointed out cannot be overlooked. The following proposals for selective eradication should be considered:

(a) Drastic localised destruction campaigns in those areas in which it has been shown that the cattle population is frequently under risk of infection because of its proximity to areas of high game density.

(b) Periodical thinning out of game population in Tribal Territories whenever necessary by opening up of area to hunters on a large scale.

(c) Maintenance of game free areas in the near vicinity of large cattle areas and along veterinary fences and cattle routes.

(d) Reduction or elimination of the elephant population by the Game Department.

(e) Initiation of a system of reporting on large-scale game movements (in Crown Lands also) inter alia to provide guidance on the effects of game on stock disease control measures. (This is now being implemented by the Veterinary Department).

14. These proposals would generally make it possible to relate hunting to the production of livestock and property as hunters would be directed to those areas where a reduction in the game population was necessary, in the same way as at present they are often directed to a cattle post where lions are reported causing damage.The demand for hunting licences is such that substantial revenue would accrue both to Government and the Tribal Treasuries and more could perhaps be made of the hides and skins industry than is at present the case. Many skins are made valueless by faulty preparation. While these measures would by no means provide the complete answer to the exacting problems of disease control they might at least reduce the present risk and provide a start from which to review progress and future policy.

Crown Lands.

15. Generally speaking the same considerations apply as in the case of Tribal Territories, except that the general poverty of the people makes game more important as a source of food and less of a threat to farming activities. It is convenient to consider separately the main areas involved.

(a) Kgalagadi. Hunting in this area is at present very rigidly controlled by constant police and administrative action. It seems apparent that a revision of this policy should be undertaken as soon as possible, particularly as the local inhabitants are very poor and the hunting of game is very important to them both economically and nutritionally. It would not be necessary to open this area to hunting by licensed European hunters as the local population is quite capable of controlling the game and should be permitted to keep this, the district's only real asset, for itself.

(b) Ghanzi. Hunting by Africans is restricted to those areas which lie outside the Game Reserve and the European farming areas. The position is the same as in the case of the Kgalagadi.

(c) Chobe and Northern Crown Lands. Cattle from Ngamiland are exported from Bushman Pits to Kazungula via Panda-ma-Tenga, because the Southern Rhodesian Veterinary Department is unwilling to accept Ngamiland cattle via Francistown it is essential that the Kazungula stock route should remain open at all times, and in view of its proximity to the Chobe Game Reserve it is necessary that a game hunting area should be maintained along its entire length, both to minimise the risk of infection and to ensure that grazing facilities are available when it is necessary to hold cattle at the boreholes. Controlled hunting expeditions could be allowed into this area.

16. Arms and Ammunition.

(a) European farming areas.

It is likely that any policy which encouraged the destruction of game would result in a move to increase the annual ammunition quota. There has already been pressure on Government to relax the existing restrictions on the importation of .303 and .22 rifles.

(b) Tribal Territories and Crown Lands.

There is already a demand for increased arms and ammunition quotas which, if satisfied, would make it unlikely that substantial further increases would be proposed as the result of a change in the game policy.

17. The restrictions on the importation of .303 and .22 rifles were imposed for several reasons, the .303 rifle being a military weapon which can be purchased comparatively cheaply and for which ammunition is readily available would present a threat to security if large numbers were held in the Territory. Moreover, because they are cheap and in ready supply they were often used by hunters who were more interested in obtaining easy supplies of game meat than in observing the conditions of these licences, and it was hoped that by imposing an almost total ban on their importation hunting would be confined to those true sportsmen who were prepared to pay higher prices for rifles of a calibre particularly suited to the hunting of the specimens which they required. There is no doubt that this policy was successful in achieving its objects because there have been few hunters in the past decade who have not been careful to observe the conditions of their licences and there were rare reports of animals being wounded because a rifle of unsuitable calibre had been used.

18. Although it will of course, be necessary to ensure as far as possible that licensed hunters use suitable rifles for the species which they wish to hunt it appears that if a new policy of closer control of game and of eradication in selected areas were adopted, it might be necessary to relax the import restrictions on .303 rifles, so as to permit of their legal use by landowners, whether in tribal territories or farming blocks, to control vermin and animals causing widespread damage.

19. An increase in demand for arms and ammunition by any section of the population would undeniably present some risk to security, though it is extremely difficult to measure it. If a policy involving greater destruction of game is adopted, it will nevertheless be necessary to reconcile its implementation with the need for strict control of arms and ammunition and some compromise will be necessary.

20. If it is decided to open large areas of the Territory for hunting, it will be worth considering whether to grant concessions to selected individuals for this purpose.This would achieve a degree of control which would help to obviate the risk referred to in paragraph 17-19 and should result in an appreciable revenue to the Territory.

21. Transmission of Diseases.

Game officials as a general rule have in the past disputed the danger of infection through the migration of game which is emphasised by those associated with the livestock industry. It has in fact been claimed in some quaters that definite proof has yet to be forthcoming that foot and mouth disease has ever been transmitted from game to domestic cattle. Apart from the fact that it is now generally accepted that game can be a contributory factor in the spread of cattle diseases this point has not been considered in detail, because economic reasons, the protection of crops and grazing, the protection of veterinary diseases control fences and the attitude of the governments of neighbouring territories themselves necessitate a review of the existing game policy as a matter of some urgency. It would nevertheless be important in determining policy to take account of factors such as the following:

(a) Is infection in game widespread?
(b) Is it endemic or does it occur only in certain conditions during a bad season?
(c) Are all animals prone to infection or only certain species?
(d) Are any species particularly susceptible?
(e) Wildebeest are for many reasons a menace to all farming activity.

22. ... It will also, however, be necessary to consider whether the Chobe or Central

Kalahari Game Reserves should be fenced and at what stage. There are many factors to consider, e.g. the desirability wherever possible of such fences following natural ecological boundaries, and their efficacy having regard to type and cost, bearing in mind that their main justification at this stage seems to be the protection of the cattle industry and this is a consideration which only becomes valid when more effective control measures are introduced outside the Game Reserves. It is noted that Game Reserves in the Republic of South Africa are now being fenced on the advice of the veterinary authorities, who state that it is essential to establish a break between the high density game population within the Game Reserves and that outside their boundaries.

Table 1. **Royal Game and Conserved Animals.**

Species	Royal Game 1961	Royal Game 1966	Conserved Animal 1967	Conserved Animal 1976	Conserved Animal 1979
Aardwolf	-	*	-	*	*
Antbear	-	*	*	*	*
Blackfooted cat	-	-	-	*	*
Brown hyaena	-	-	*	*	*
Cheetah	*	*	*	*	*
Chobe bushbuck	*	*	-	-	-
Civet	-	-	-	*	*
Eland	*	*	-	-	-
Elephant (female and immature)	*	*	-	-	-
Giraffe	*	*	*	*	*
Hippopotamus	*	*	*	*	*
Honey badger	-	-	*	*	*
Klipspringer	*	*	*	*	*
Mountain reedbuck	-	-	-	*	*
Night ape (lesser galago)	-	-	-	*	*
Oribi	*	*	*	*	*
Otter	-	-	-	*	*
Pangolin	-	-	*	*	*
Puku	*	*	*	*	*
Roan antelope	*	*	-	*	*
Rock dassie	-	-	-	-	*
Rhinoceros	*	*	*	*	*
Sable antelope	*	*	-	-	-
Serval	-	-	-	*	*
Sharpe's steenbok	-	-	-	-	*
Vaal rhebok	*	*	-	*	*
Waterbuck	*	*	-	*	*
Yellow-spotted dassie	-	-	*	*	*
Kgori bustard	-	-	-	*	*
Narina trogon	-	-	-	-	*
Stanley bustard	-	-	-	*	*
all buzzards	-	-	-	-	*
all cranes	-	-	-	*	*
all eagles	-	-	-	*	*
all egrets	-	-	-	*	*
all falcons	-	-	-	-	*
all flamingoes	-	-	-	*	*
Fish owl	-	-	-	*	*
all goshawks	-	-	-	-	*

Table 1. continued.

Species	Royal Game 1961	Royal Game 1966	Conserved Animal 1967	Conserved Animal 1976	Conserved Animal 1979
Hammerkop	-	-	-	*	*
all harriers	-	-	-	-	*
all herons	-	-	-	*	*
all ibises	-	-	-	-	*
all jacanas	-	-	-	*	*
all kites	-	-	-	-	*
all pelicans	-	-	-	*	*
all sparrowhawks	-	-	-	-	*
all storks	-	-	-	*	*
Secretary bird	-	-	-	*	*
Spoonbill	-	-	-	*	*
all vultures	-	-	-	*	*
Python	-	-	-	-	*
Total species/ groups:	14	16	12	37	48

Table 2. **Tribally conserved animals.**

Species:	Principal Law	Ngwato	Tawana	Kwena	Ngwaketse	Kgatla
Tribe:	Principal Law	Ngwato	Tawana	Kwena	Ngwaketse	Kgatla
Enactment:	Act 47/ 1967	SI. 64/ 1967	SI. 65/ 1967	SI. 37/ 1968	SI. 56/ 1968	SI. 106/ 1973
Species:	-	-	-	Aardwolf	-	-
Antbear	-	-	-	-	-	-
Brown hyaena	-	-	-	-	-	-
	-	-	-	-	-	Bushbuck
Cheetah		*	*	-	-	-
	-	-	-	-	Eland	Eland
Giraffe		*	*	-	-	-
Hippopotamus		*	*	-	-	-
	-	-	-	-	Hedgehog	-
Honey badger	-	-	-	-	-	-
Klipspringer		*	-	-	-	-
	-	-	-	-	Kudu	-
	-	-	Leopard[1]	-	-	-
	-	Mountain reedbuck[2]	-	*	*	-
Oribi	-	-	-	-	-	-
Pangolin	-	-	-	-	-	-
Puku	-	-	-	-	-	-
	-	-	-	Reedbuck	-	Reedbuck
Rhinoceros	-	-	*	-		
	-	-	Roan[3]	-	-	-
	-	-	Waterbuck[4]	-	-	-
Yellow-spotted dassie	-	-	-	-	-	-
	-	-	Zebra[1]	-	-	-
	-	-	-	-	-	all ducks
	-	-	-	-	-	all geese
	-	-	-	-	Kori bustard	-
	-	-	-	-	Lesser korhaan	-
	-	-	-	-	Owl	-
	-	-	-	-	Secretary bird	-
	-	-	-	-	all storks	-
	-	-	-	-	-	Python
	-	all bird eggs[2]	*[3]	-	-	all bird eggs

1 Deleted 1970; 2 Added 1970; 3 Added 1970; 4 Added 1971.

Table 3. **Tribally protected species.**

Tribe:	Principal Law	Ngwato	Tawana	Kwena	Ngwaketse	Kgatla
Enactment:	Act 47/1967	SI. 64/1967	SI. 65/1967	SI. 37/1968	SI. 56/1968	SI. 106/1973
Species: Aardwolf		-	-	-	-	-
	-	-	-	-	Bat-eared fox	-
	-	-	Buffalo[7]	-	-	-
	Bushbuck	-	*[8]	*[7]	-	-
	-	-	-	-	Caracal[9]	-
	Eland	*	*	*	-	-
	Elephant[2] (immature and females)	Elephant	Elephant	-	-	-
	-	Gemsbok	*[7]	*	*	*
	-	-	-	-	Genet[9]	-
	-	-	*[7]	-	-	Hartebeest
	Klipspringer[1]	Kudu	*[7]	*	-	*
	-	-	Lechwe[7]	-	-	-
	-	Leopard	*[5]	*	*	*
	Lion[3]	*	*[5]	*	*	*
	-	Ostrich	*[7]	*	*	*
	-	Reedbuck	*[7]	-	-	-
	Rhebok[3]	-	-	-	-	-
	Roan	*	*[6]	-	-	-
	Sable	*	*	-	-	-
	-	-	Sitatunga[7]	-	-	-
	-	-	-	-	Silver fox[9]	-
	-	Springbok[4]	*[7]	-	-	-
	-	Tsessebe	*[7]	-	-	-
	-	-	-	-	Warthog[9]	-
	Waterbuck[3]	-	*[5]	-	-	-
	-	-	-	-	-	Wildebeest

1 Deleted SI. 9/1968; 2 Amended to Elephant cows with calves at foot SI. 16/1968; 3 Deleted SI. 16/1968; 4 Part area only; 5 Added SI. 33/1970; 6 Deleted SI. 33/1970; 7 Added SI. 43/1971; 8 Added SI. 44/1971; 9 Added SI. 40/1975.

Table 4. **Protected game 1979.**

Chobe bushbuck
Eland
Elephant cows with calves at foot
Leopard
Lion
Sable antelope.

Table 5. **Allowable hunting quotas 1979–1987, Single Game (=large game) Licences.**

Year:	1979	1980	1981	1982	1983	1984	1985	1986	1987
Species									
Baboon	0	0	0	0	0	0	0	20[1]	260
Buffalo	2010	1751	1755	1546	1457	1520	1485	1314	1359
Bushbuck	115	36	36	36	35	35	40	40	38
Crocodile	109	123	168	168	138	138	55	50	57
Duiker	37114	10037	10007	10412	460[2]	89	123	150	284
Eland	1928	1347	1324	1319	1193	1211	1218	309	360
Elephant	567	448	396	104	0	0	0	0	0
Gemsbok	4647	2426	4063	4013	3941	3951	3650	3168	3887
Genet	0	0	0	0	0	0	0	0	260[1]
Hartebeest	18810	11693	11908	12128	13177	13677	11040	1054	798
Impala	4563	2383	2770	2415	2420	2473	2638	2396	2480
Jackal	0	0	0	0	0	0	0	0	260[1]
Kudu	3522	2310	2834	2804	2664	2590	3168	2315	2252
Lechwe	1305	440	535	505	505	524	496	522	508
Leopard	222	219	219	210	203	197	78	79	103
Lion	269	338	344	342	294	299	269	139	173
Monkey	0	0	0	0	0	0	0	0	160[1]
Ostrich	6571	3421	3551	3261	3264	2713	2953	1888	2030
Porcupine	0	0	0	0	0	0	0	0	260[1]
Reedbuck	313	257	257	252	252	264	232	264	262
Sable	149	67	67	67	76	78	170	88	104
Sitatunga	254	204	204	194	188	205	219	217	235
Spotted hyaena	0	0	0	0	0	0	0	20[1]	260
Springbok	10150	4135	4165	3740	3615	4018	3765	1810	4180
Steenbok	0	0	0	11461[3]	513[2]	23	223	133	314
Tsessebe	1275	634	639	606	663	708	700	411	406
Warthog	3320	1608	1583	1473	1420	1304	1658	1170	1232
Wildcat	0	0	0	0	0	0	0	0	260[1]
Wild dog	0	0	0	0	0	0	0	0	260[1]
Wildebeest	23095	10680	12088	12295	13948	14557	11732	2405	960
Zebra	1900	2005	2715	2580	2440	2439	2430	1995	2105
Total 'A'[4]	85094	46525	51621	50058	51893	52901	47996	21634	23529
Total 'B'[5]	122208	56562	61628	71931	52866	53013	48342	21937	26007

1 Non-citizen hunters, others take it on the Small Game Licence.
2 Citizen quota transferred to Small Game Licence (=unlimited).
3 Citizen quota transferred from Small Game Licence.
4 Totals of species offered throughout.
5 Totals taking into account additions and deletions.

Addendum

Part I. Note 16.

This question was resolved in 1984 by the Interpretation Act which defined the difference as follows: "In an enactment "shall" shall be construed as imperative and "may" as permissive and empowering." (Section 45).

Part I. Note 22bis.

The Bechuanaland Protectorate Penal Code of 1964 replaced unwritten substantive Roman-Dutch criminal law and defined the status of wild animals with respect to "Things Capable of Being Stolen" as follows:

"Wild animals in the enjoyment of their natural liberty are not capable of being stolen; but a wild animal which is usually kept in confinement and which is the property of any person is capable of being stolen so long as it is in confinement, or, if it escapes, so long as it has not regained its natural liberty.

"A wild animal is deemed to be in confinement if it is confined in a den, cage, sty, tank or other small enclosure, or is otherwise so placed that its owner can exercise effective control over it.

"A wild animal which has escaped from confinement is deemed to have regained its natural liberty if it has escaped from sight or if, although it is still in sight, its pursuit is difficult." (Subsections 263(4),(5),(6).

Subsection 263(6) is almost a literal translation from Justinian's Institutes.